A SPACE TRAVELER'S GUIDE TO MARS

A SPACE TRAVELER'S
GUIDE TO ARS

by Dr. I. M. Levitt, Director of the Fels
Planetarium of The Franklin Institute

Illustrated with Line Drawings and Photographs

Henry Holt and Company

New York

To Alice,
whose inspiration and understanding
made this book possible

Foreword

From time immemorial travel and discovery have called with strange insistence to him who, wondering on the world, felt adventure in his veins. The leaving familiar sights and faces to push forth into the unknown has with magnetic force drawn the bold to great endeavor and fired the thought of those who stayed at home.

Percival Lowell—*Mars and Its Canals,* 1906

Fifty years have passed since the great explorer of Mars completed his exhaustive telescopic survey of the red planet. Today science at the mid-century presents an overwhelmingly impressive panorama. All around us we see developments and technological achievements which in Lowell's day were but dreams of the most imaginative. Yet, in this day these achievements are part of our lives. They point to the time when the physical exploration of space will commence. With this step will come the conquest of the nearer planets.

Is this adventure coming in our own future? The answer is an exciting yes. The march of astronautics under the irresistible pressures of guided missile developments makes certain that many who read this book will be involved in space travel during their lives. Some of the readers will hear of great expeditions taking off from space stations high above the surface of the earth to travel to the planets; this at the turn of the century. And one of the targets in our sights must be Mars.

In this work of the future astronomy will play a major role. For in astronomy the day of the simple, unadorned telescope, as used by Lowell, is at an end. Today, we find spectroscopy, television, photoelectric photometry, radiometry, etc., playing significant roles in the advancement of this science and nowhere is the application of these auxiliaries more apparent than in planetary investigation.

As this arsenal is brought to bear on Mars, many of the questions raised at the turn of the century have been resolved or have been better understood. The red planet stands in the sky as a challenge. This challenge the scientist accepts and in essence what follows is the picture of Mars as we understand it today and what we may find when we land there.

I. M. LEVITT

The Fels Planetarium, Philadelphia
August 3, 1956

Contents

A SPACE TRAVELER'S GUIDE TO MARS

1

↑

Men against Mars

You are a space traveler whether you know it or not. At this very moment you are moving at a speed which should leave you breathless, in a direction which is determined by the many different directions of a set of giddy motions.

Nonsense! you say. I'm here on earth, and it's the steadiest place in the universe. I'm not moving!

Yes, you are. Let's see just what your motions are. To begin, the earth spins on its axis, once around each 24 hours. If you were at the equator, this would give you a speed of more than 1000 miles an hour. Of course it's more likely that you're somewhere between the equator and one of the earth's poles. Say you're in a midnorthern latitude such as that of the United States. Then your speed, because of the rotation of the earth, is only about 750 miles an hour—and this is just about the speed of sound.

But now consider the fact that the earth is circling the sun, once around each year. We are not aware of this motion, except by careful study and experiment; otherwise it would not have taken 3000 years to discover it. This

3

orbital motion of the earth is fast—18½ miles per second, or 66,600 miles per hour! But don't go away; we have more.

The solar family—the sun and its planets—is moving with respect to its neighborhood. The sun is like one bee in a swarm, moving in the same general direction with the rest of the swarm, but at the same time moving with respect to the other members of the swarm. The sun is moving toward a point in the constellation Hercules, not too far away from the bright summer star Vega in Lyra. In this direction the speed is 43,000 miles per hour. As the sun heads with his speed in this direction in space, it carries the earth and all the other planets along with it.

And there's still more. The sun and its neighborhood—the "swarm" we spoke of earlier—are revolving around the center of the Milky Way system, the great congeries of stars of which the sun is but one member, with a speed of 175 miles per second—630,000 miles per hour. This is the last cosmic motion of which we have any certain knowledge, but now man is trying to add another dimension.

Hardy pioneers are working toward the end of taking off into space in a direction away from the earth's surface—trying to crash through the last frontier of the earth's gravitational bond, to explore the moon and the other planets. Make no mistake; in the near future this will be done and you or somebody you know will partake of this motion to go gliding off into space as space travelers.

The author has presented cogent arguments in many articles to indicate that the establishment of an unmanned satellite in the very near future is highly probable. The July 25, 1955, White House announcement of "Project

Vanguard" puts the date at 1957 or 1958. This will be the beginning of man's struggle for the conquest of space.

The atmosphere for space travel is becoming more favorable. No longer are there the hostile and withering judgments passed against the advocates of space travel. Today space travel has attained maturity and, with promise of government subsidy, an astonishing degree of respectability. And when it materializes, adventurers will once more go exploring for new lands—the moon first, and then some more hospitable place.

There is a new land in the sky that will certainly be attacked as soon as possible. Interestingly it has just about the same area as the land area of the earth. This land is Mars, the subject of space-travel stories for generations, the subject of innumerable questions by scientists and laymen alike.

Fifty or even 25 years ago the idea of travel to Mars was considered so unlikely that no qualified scientist would discuss it. Today it is not a question of *can* we travel to Mars. Today the question is *when* are we going to Mars.

To explore Mars will take more than space ships. It will require a twenty-first-century Columbus with more courage and ability than it is right to expect of a mortal. But even today plans are being made for expeditions to Mars. Even as this is being written, you may read of scientists mapping proposals destined to land human beings on Mars. The most ambitious of these proposals is that of a former German rocket expert, Dr. Wernher von Braun, the co-designer of the deadly V-2 rocket and today technical director of the Redstone Arsenal in Huntsville, Alabama.

In his book *The Mars Project* Dr. von Braun in 1953 fully documented a proposal to reach Mars. Von Braun is perhaps best known for his advocacy of a space station circling the earth at a height of 1075 miles, but his Mars project is infinitely more ambitious. In terms of money, materials, and man power the Mars project would be the greatest undertaking of man in his entire history. The scope of this project makes the development of the B-52 bomber appear as simple as the repair of a leaky faucet! And the most significant aspect of this whole trip is that it can be consummated in the near future without the necessity for a major technological breakthrough, though if a breakthrough does occur it will accelerate our time scale.

Essentially von Braun breaks down the problem into three parts. The first is the assembling of an armada of space ships on earth, to carry to the space station the necessary materials with which to construct the fleet that will go to Mars. The second step is the trip through space to an orbit around Mars. The third is the landing on Mars and the return to the armada circling around Mars. If these three steps are accomplished, the return to earth should not present too many difficulties.

If the public was staggered by the first proposal to build a space station circling the earth, this more elaborate proposal is simply overwhelming in a technical sense. The project is of such titanic proportions that it will probably be consummated only on an international scale.

Let's examine the details of this project and visualize it as means to get you, a space traveler, to Mars.

To begin, von Braun would assemble on earth 46 cargo ships, each weighing 6400 tons! This is about the weight of a medium-sized ocean liner or a light cruiser. Each cargo ship, when blasted from earth into the path that will permit it to circle the earth every two hours, will consume fuel at a fantastic rate—56 tons per second! This tonnage is about what the average motorist uses in 15 years of normal travel.

Upon reaching the space station, each 6400-ton space ship will have shrunk to about 39 tons! In other words, for each pound put into the sky 165 pounds of fuel and "hardware" must be used.

Once the cargo ships have assembled the necessary material at the space station, a fleet of ten space ships will be constructed to make the trip to Mars. These will weigh 3700 tons each and will contain the necessary fuels, equipment, and provisions for a party of 70 people.

As the weight of the ten space ships will total about 37,000 tons, it means that 950 loads netting 39 tons each must be made from earth to the space station, to concentrate the materials to make the expedition possible. Of course this assumes that nothing goes wrong with any of the transports during the nine months of incessant work that von Braun estimates for the job.

The ten space ships would aim to end up in an orbit circling Mars and then three landing craft, each weighing 200 tons, would be launched for the purpose of exploring the surface of Mars. An exploration party of 50 men, with complete provisions and equipment for a stay of 400 days on Mars, would spiral down to the surface; the remaining 20 men would stay in the space ships circling Mars.

The first of the landing craft would come down on skids, on the polar cap of Mars, which von Braun believed to be covered with snow. Actually, as we shall see later, the best evidence tells us that there is little snow on Mars, but this is a trivial matter; wheels can easily replace the skids. The crew of this first landing craft would bring out special trucks and travel toward the equator of Mars, there to prepare a landing field for the other two craft, a field that would then serve as the operations base for the exploration of the planet.

Following the exploration of the surface, one of the landing craft would be abandoned on Mars. The other two would be abandoned as soon as the explorers have gained the security of the space armada circling Mars. Finally the ten space ships with all personnel would head back to the earth space station with their mission accomplished after two years 239 days.

Here is a detailed plan for a trip to Mars. Of course it may take too much for granted, here and there, but still the plan is supported by a wealth of experimental and technical data. Other plans have been advanced, some rather sketchy and visionary, others complete and detailed to accomplish the same purpose. However, the goal finally is reached; these plans are proof that the intellect of man is ready to contend with the realities of a trip to Mars.

There have been plans for *unmanned* expeditions to Mars, to provide the information necessary to plan intelligently the program of later explorers. A plan has been devised whereby a completely automatic Mars satellite may be projected to Mars from the terrestrial space station, to telemeter back to earth significant information about the Martian surface and atmosphere.

Two British engineers have developed a plan called "The Martian Probe." They propose a three-step rocket—

one that would drop two of its sections, one at a time, as their fuel load was exhausted along the way. Each section would have a mass-ratio of 4.2. This means that the fuel in each section would weigh 4.2 times as much as the "hardware." The whole assembly would blast off from the earth's surface with a total weight of more than 700 tons, and would lose its two sections and so much of the fuel of the third section that the final weight, in an orbit 10,000 miles above the surface of Mars, would be about half a ton. Theoretically this is possible, but few engineers have much faith in any space-travel undertaking in which the earth's surface is the starting point.

Present thinking is that use must be made of an earth-circling space station as a launching platform for either the Martian Probe or a manned trip to Mars. Once this station is established, the possibility of putting the Probe in the Martian sky is considerably enhanced. In fact, there are many scientists who believe that it will be easier to put a satellite in a path around Mars than it will be to put a space station in our sky!

The Martian Probe would contain a solar generating unit to produce power to transmit information back to earth. We are already accustomed to television and even higher-resolution facsimile transmission here on earth; the Probe would scan the surface of Mars in strips about 200 miles wide, with a TV camera attached to a telescope, and the entire surface would be covered in about six weeks. Instantaneously, of course, this information would be transmitted to earth, arriving a few minutes later, and revealing objects as small as 1000 feet in diameter.

The vertical height of the Probe, the surface temperature of Mars, atmospheric pressures, contours of the surface, and other similar information would be determined by familiar equipment such as that used in meteorological balloons today. By conventional coded-pulse techniques, these bits of information would be transmitted to earth. All these factors on which the success of a manned Martian expedition would depend would be determined in advance, and then the von Braun proposal, or some variant of it, could become a reality.

While still perhaps 50 years away from this adventure, man today is developing and discussing schemes to make it come true. When the time is right, the great expedition will not be delayed and confused by a multiplicity of proposals; it will move along swiftly because it has been thoroughly boiled down into a single project of many facets which can be altered as need arises, within the framework of a single concept.

To understand the magnitude of this undertaking, it may be helpful to get a notion of how Mars is situated in space. A model would be of value.

Let's begin in New York City, where the Empire State Building stands. Let's put the sun there, and shrink the sun's 865,000-mile diameter to the height of the Empire State Building—about 1400 feet. From this 1400-foot sphere we must move out about 11 miles—say, south and west to Newark, New Jersey—to put a five-foot sphere which represents the planet Mercury, whose real distance from the sun is over 36,000,000 miles.

The next planet, Venus, is 7700 miles in diameter and is located about 65,000,000 miles from the sun; in our model a 12½-foot ball in Linden, New Jersey, about 20 miles from New York, would do nicely. The earth, 7900

miles in diameter and 93,000,000 miles from the sun,
would be represented by a 12.8-foot sphere in New Bruns-
wick, New Jersey, 29 miles from New York.

Mars, 4200 miles in diameter and 141,000,000 miles
from the sun, could be a 6.8-foot ball at Princeton, 43
miles from New York.

Now we take a big jump to get to the giant planet Jupiter, 88,000 miles in diameter and 480,000,000 miles from
the sun. A ball 142 feet in diameter in Sunbury, Pennsylvania, 150 miles from New York, could represent this
planet. A 126-foot ball in Johnstown, Pennsylvania, 276
miles from New York, would represent Saturn, whose actual diameter is 77,000 miles and whose distance from sun
is 885,000,000 miles. The rings of Saturn would be about
300 feet in diameter and one inch thick.

About twice as far from the sun—1,785,000,000 miles—
is the planet Uranus, with a diameter of 30,000 miles;
we'll use a ball 48 feet in diameter in Lima, Ohio, 550
miles from New York. Neptune would be a ball 45 feet
in diameter in Peoria, Illinois, 870 miles from New York;
this planet, 28,000 miles in diameter, is 2,797,000,000 miles
from the sun.

Finally, the most distant known planet, Pluto, with a
diameter of probably about 3600 miles and a real distance
from the sun of 3,670,000,000 miles, would be a ball six
feet in diameter in Kansas City, Missouri, 1150 miles from
New York.

On this scale the nearest star would again be a ball
about 1500 feet in diameter, at a distance of about 32 times
that of our moon or 8,000,000 miles from the earth!

The distances of the planets differ considerably from

each other, and in this we can begin to see how it might be that life might exist on certain planets, and not on others. One of the planets which did provide an equable home for life is, of course, the earth. The other planet definitely known to support some kind of life is Mars, and there are more questions asked about Mars and other life than about any other object in the sky. Let's examine a typical scene.

It is a warm August night, and the public is admitted to the observatory. The giant telescope is aimed at a garnet jewel in the sky, and columns of visitors wind toward the eyepiece of the instrument. A man at the head of the line looks into the eyepiece, then moves his head slightly to one side, and looks up at Mars with the naked eye. He points a finger to the sky and asks, "Is that Mars, that bright red star there?"

When he receives an affirmative answer, he again looks into the eyepiece, this time with renewed interest. In a few seconds he steps aside and another takes his place, to pass through approximately the same routine.

It is getting late, and soon the observatory will close. Little knots of people cluster at various spots on the observatory floor, talking in muted tones. Someone approaches the astronomer in charge and asks, "Are the polar caps made of ice? Why couldn't they be made of carbon dioxide—dry ice, that is?" Before an answer can be given to these questions, another one is thrown out: "Is there oxygen in the atmosphere of Mars?"

As question after question is answered, the scattered groups gravitate toward the astronomer. Everyone is listening. Then someone asks, "Is there life on Mars?" and everyone breathes softly, so as not to miss the answer to the question that really has been uppermost in everyone's mind. Only the buttery sound of the driving mechanism of the telescope disturbs the silence.

The visitors hang on every word of what the astronomer says in reply. He speaks of atmospheres, water, vegetation, clouds, time, temperatures. Time after time he is interrupted by "How do you know?" "What proof is there?" "Can't something else produce the same results?" Patiently the astronomer tries to answer all the questions, but always there is a feeling that there is so much to say and so little time. Invariably someone will ask, "Isn't it possible to have life different from ours—something maybe based on silicon, instead of on carbon?" Once more the astronomer begins to explain, giving the criteria for life as we know it, yet at the same time admitting that life in other forms may possibly exist. This starts the questioning anew, everyone trying to build a living being to fit any environment, however extreme. The group of visitors from all walks and professions assumes a homogeneity sparked by their common interest in life on other worlds.

Presently the questioning stops, as visitors realize the lateness of the hour. The nightly show, with Mars as the principal actor, is over. But this is no rare occurrence. Every two years, when Mars is closest to the earth and shines as a bright star in our sky, visitors come to observatories to ask these same questions. Why is there so much interest in Mars? Is it because a half century or more ago there were some astronomers who believed that perhaps Mars was the abode of life? And if it is other life we are looking for—why? What is there about planets in general and Mars in particular that excites the imagination of the average man? No one can know all of the answers to these questions, but the various facets of them make for fascinating speculation.

The philosopher of old and the modern scientist alike have known the question "Is there life on other worlds?" In the recent years of the "flying saucer" sightings many believed this question to be answered. Every unexplained phenomenon—better, every phenomenon which the *untutored* viewer could not immediately explain—was instantly interpreted as a sign that malevolent extraterrestrial visitors were about to pay us an unwelcome visit. Why creatures from other planets must be "malevolent," in view of the wicked things that occur on earth, no one can quite explain!

Eventually a time will come when all the answers to the questions about life on Mars will be forthcoming, and at least partial answers to the general question of life on other worlds. But speculation can carry us only so far.

Man does speculate, even about the origins of the universe. But today we can find organization in only half of the material of the universe, the remainder being stuff with which we are also familiar, so we discuss it, too. Somehow or other, around at least one star, our sun, there came into being cold bodies we call the planets.

Two planets in the system, omitting the earth, have physical conditions permitting at least some marginal form of life. One such planet is Venus, enveloped in such a deep and dense atmosphere that we can know little or nothing of its surface.

The other planet is Mars—the subject of this book.

2

↑

The Nearest Land

Beyond the orbit of the earth Mars travels its path around the sun at an average distance of 141,000,000 miles, a trifle over one and a half times the earth's distance from the sun. For a few months every two years Mars appears as an orange, or dull-red, bright star in the southern night sky; if observed diligently, it seems to sweep majestically against the background of the stars, first to the east, then to the west, and finally toward the east once more, taking many weeks to complete the cycle.

Actually Mars is not the fastest moving of the bright planets. Venus, coming closer to the earth and also being nearer the sun, moves faster. But because Venus is closer to the sun than the earth, it can never be seen more than about three and a half hours after sunset or the same interval before sunrise. Mars, however, revolving in an orbit larger than ours, can be seen in the midnight sky and can be studied through the night.

Because of the rapid motion of Mars it can readily be seen to retrograde or move westward against the stars,

15

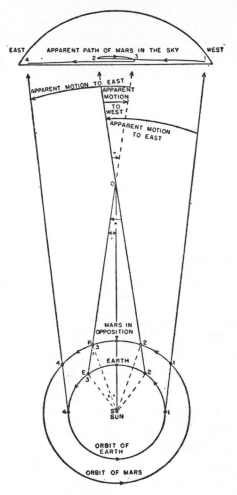

The reason for the backward or retrograde motion of Mars can be seen from this diagram. When the earth goes halfway around the sun in six months, Mars only goes a quarter of the way around. Lines connect the positions of the planets in this period, and the more rapid motion of the earth is reflected in the retrograde motion of the planet. (*Courtesy of Dr. C. H. Cleminshaw*, Griffith Observer)

though in reality this is only an apparent motion due to the combination of the motions of Mars and the earth.

Mars does not actually move backward against the background of stars; this apparent backward motion is caused by the combination of the motions of Mars and the earth. Its motion is always forward; that is, if we could look down on the solar system from the north pole of the sky, Mars would always circle the sun in a counterclockwise direction. When Mars is just halfway across the sky and stands at its highest point at midnight, the sun, the earth, and Mars are in a line in that order, and Mars is said to be in opposition. The earth has been overtaking Mars and at just that instant it passes Mars. However, some time earlier Mars begins to appear to move westward against the background of stars as though it were retracing its steps.

Let's see just why this is so. Imagine that you are on an express train speeding along at a rapid pace. Imagine also that on an adjacent track there is a freight train lazily moving in the same direction. Now when the express train passes the freight train, the latter appears to move backward. This illusion, of course, is caused by the slower speed of the freight, for both trains are moving in the same direction. In the sky the earth is the fast express and Mars is the slow freight.

Appearance and Physical Characteristics

To the naked eye Mars can be a magnificently bright object. Its brightness depends on its nearness to the earth and also on the position of Mars with respect to its perihelion point, the point in its orbit closest to the sun. The bright-

ness of Mars at the most favorable opposition is about
100 times that of Polaris, the North Star. With this magnitude Mars can become the fourth brightest object in
the sky. Only the sun, moon, and Venus can be brighter
than Mars at this favorable opposition. On the other hand,
at an unfavorable opposition Mars may be only 20 times
as bright as the North Star, which makes Mars fainter than
the star Sirius but still a bright object in the sky.

Seen with the naked eye Mars appears as a bright star,
but with a telescope the fascinating surface details of the
planet can be discerned. The planet can never appear large
in a telescope using moderate magnifications simply because it is so small and so far away. With a large telescope,
using a power of 500, the size of the planet disk can become appreciable. Let us assume that the planet is at its
most favorable opposition. At this minimum distance the
planet has an apparent angular diameter of 25 seconds of
arc, which is the size of a dime as seen from 480 feet. Using a power of 500 will make the image appear three and
a half degrees in diameter. This makes Mars about seven
times the size of the full moon, which is the size of a dime
at about one foot.

Suppose the moon is visible and you have available a
pair of seven-power binoculars. Turn them on the moon
and you will be surprised at the detail you can see. Now
imagine that you are at an observatory with its large telescope, looking at Mars with a magnification of 500. Here
you will begin to see detail on Mars. There is, however,
one important difference. When a celestial object is magnified 500 times, the atmospheric disturbances are magnified by the same factor. Therefore, while we should see a

good bit of detail on Mars, as we shall presently learn, it is only occasionally that Mars can be seen as well as the moon with seven-power binoculars, although the images may be of the same diameter.

Unfortunately there are very few places on this earth where observing conditions are good enough to use the telescope at its maximum efficiency. Because we live at the bottom of an ocean of live, turbulent atmosphere, all the light which comes to us from the celestial objects is affected by this unsteadiness. If the air is very turbulent, the image of the planet will dance around wildly, and as a result comparatively little will be seen. The astronomer calls this "bad seeing." This effect is experienced in our everyday lives. You see this in looking at something over a hot radiator in the winter, and in summer all you have to do is look down a hot road in the full heat of day to appreciate the effects of turbulence.

When the seeing settles down and the turbulence has momentarily subsided, the image appears clear and sharp and the fine, intricate surface markings of the planet can be observed.

This also explains why photography may never be the solution to delineating fine detail on a planet's surface. To photograph a planet a time exposure is necessary, because photographically the planet is a faint object. During the exposure the light from the planet collects on the plate and is stored. An instant of bad seeing, even though the remainder of the exposure is good, destroys the fine detail on the plate. The only way to overcome this is to make the exposure times so short that the plate will catch only those moments of good seeing.

The astronomer's hope is that photographic emulsions will become so fast that time exposures of a twentieth of a second or shorter will be adequate. With these short exposures good photographs taken at the time of good seeing can yield sharp images. This also points up why visual observations are far superior to present-day photographs. The eye can detect faint detail and intricate markings because the eye can see the image when the seeing is at its best during that tiny time interval. The image on the retina can go directly to the brain, and the impression will be one in which the fine detail will be perceived. While the eye has a tremendous advantage over the photographic plate in seeing these markings, it has one great disadvantage—and that is, if the markings are too faint to register on the retina, they are invisible. For this reason photographic plates which record light for a considerable interval disclose more features than the eye, though not with such fine detail.

Recent experiments directed toward the development of an electronic telescope will yield a device which will electronically amplify the well-detailed image of Mars to permit extremely short exposures. In this device the image formed by the large lens or mirror of the telescope is captured on a supersensitive television camera tube. This electronic picture can then be made much brighter. Existing commercial television equipment is not suitable because the coarseness of a picture that will satisfy the home viewer is in no wise satisfactory for scientific purposes, but special equipment has been devised and used with exciting and promising results.

Because Mars lies outside the orbit of the earth and cannot come between the earth and the sun, it cannot undergo phases like our moon or Venus. Nevertheless the disk is not round at all times—a phenomenon discerned by Galileo in December, 1610. At quadrature, when Mars is off to the side of the earth, it can appear in the gibbous phase about like our moon 11 or 12 days old. At this phase a sixth or a seventh of Mars will be invisible. The phase angle—that is, the angle at Mars between the earth and the sun—is 47 degrees. It is in this phase that Mars shows a noticeable twilight effect and the terminator, the line dividing the night half from the day half of the planet, is fuzzy.

Twilight on the earth is a period when we cannot see the sun but the sun still illuminates our surroundings. As viewed from another planet this twilight zone of the earth would be seen to be 16 degrees wide on the earth's surface. From the earth we see the twilight zone on Mars as eight degrees wide. This knowledge, at times, permits the height of the scattering atmosphere of Mars to be determined.

The height of the atmosphere, which will be covered in detail in subsequent sections, is governed by the gravitational field of Mars. With a diameter of 4215 miles (with an uncertainty of only ten miles), Mars has about half the diameter of the earth.

It is possible by timing the moons or satellites of Mars to determine the mass of the planet. At the observed distances of the satellites from Mars the periods would be different if the mass of Mars were different. The period-distance relationship uniquely determines the mass of Mars, which happens to be 0.1076 times that of the earth. The combined smaller diameter and lower mass yield a force of

gravity for the planet 0.38 times that of the earth. The
volume of the planet is 0.150 that of the earth. The density of Mars is considerably less than the earth's. Compared
to an average density of 5.52 for the earth, Mars has a
density of 3.96. The escape velocity for Mars is 3.1 miles
per second—which means that if the atmosphere of Mars
were not present, a meteor falling to its surface from an
infinite distance would strike Mars with a speed of 3.1
miles per second. By the same token, if you were on Mars
and tried to shoot something off its surface, that something
would also be endowed with a speed of 3.1 miles per second. Now let's see what all these numbers mean.

The lower value for the pull of gravity will make a 200-
pound man on the earth weigh 76 pounds on Mars. However, the earth man has the same muscle strength on Mars,
which means that if a 200-pound man on the earth can
lift his own weight, on Mars he will be able to lift 500
pounds! Quite a problem on the earth but not on Mars.
On Mars every man will be a superman!

The velocity of escape has an intriguing feature, for it
is less than half of the velocity of escape from the earth and
about 0.6 the velocity we need to establish a space platform
to circle the earth. Some of the rocket hardware in use
today could either provide a space platform for Mars or,
more practically, be used to reach one of its moons—which
in turn would be used to leave Mars for interplanetary
travel. The more the space-minded scientist contemplates
this the more certain he is to conclude that we live on the
wrong planet!

The lower density of Mars gives rise to several theories
of the internal structure, and these have been the subject

of considerable speculation and debate. Sir Harold Jeffreys believes the center of Mars to consist of an iron core with a radius of about 850 miles. Overlying this is a mantle of magnesium and iron silicate about 375 miles thick, and overlying that is a mantle of magnesium silicate 875 miles thick. In this fashion Jeffreys extends to the planets the results which he obtained for the earth from seismological and geochemical studies. Dr. Harold Urey, on the other hand, holds for a planet with a homogeneous structure: that is, for a structure without any layers or abrupt changes. As we shall presently see, the oblateness of Mars is greater than for the earth, which is also indicative of a more nearly homogeneous body. At the equator of Mars the centrifugal force is 1/219 of the force of gravity. The ratio of oblateness to centrifugal force is so near the theoretical limit for a homogeneous planet that Urey's concept has substantial support.

Like the earth Mars has an equatorial bulge. The polar diameter of the earth is smaller than the equatorial diameter by one part in 297. In the case of Mars this flattening is more pronounced. The polar diameter is smaller than the equatorial diameter by one part in 192. This value, determined by H. Struve, results from the observations of the satellites. The equatorial bulge of a planet causes the line of nodes—the points of intersection of the equator of Mars with the orbits of the satellites—of the satellite to rotate in the plane of the equator. This motion is uniform and is related to the flattening. The satellites of Mars are so close to its surface that this method can be used to yield precise results.

The observed flattening turns out to be more than twice

the dynamical flattening. This is a curious feature which at this time is not yet understood. Astronomers believe that there is something basically wrong about the measuring of an atmosphere laden planet. Some believe the actual measures may introduce a spurious oblateness. This remains a challenging problem and is unlikely to be settled for some time.

Because Mars has a thin atmosphere, its albedo, or reflecting power, is low. Mars reflects about 15 per cent of the incident solar radiation compared to 35 to 40 per cent for the earth with its extensive cloud cover. This makes Mars a reflector twice as good as the moon and somewhat less than one half as good as the earth. Further, because Mars is red, its photographic albedo is quite low. Mars is believed to absorb 90 per cent of the short-wave or bluish solar radiations.

The rotation period of the planet has been fully determined to an accuracy of 1/10,000 of a second from comparatively recent observations. In the past a drawing of Mars made by the Dutch mathematician and astronomer Christian Huygens on November 28, 1659, at 7:00 P.M. was used in conjunction with latter drawings to determine the length of the day.

By 1666 the French astronomer Jean Dominique Cassini had determined the period as 24 hours and 40 minutes. What a sensation it must have created at that time for them to discover that not only did Mars have a day but it was almost of the same length as the day of the earth! Today the diurnal period of Mars as referred to the stars, or a fixed direction in space, is given as 24 hours, 37 minutes, 22.6679 seconds! Dr. Joseph Ashbrook, of the Harvard Observatory, has collected material from many sources and has arrived at the above figure for the rotation period of Mars. In fact, so precise is this figure and so sure is Dr. Ashbrook that it is invariable that he has suggested it could be used to determine fluctuations in the length of the terrestrial day, which referred to the stars is 23 hours, 56 minutes, 4 seconds. Of course we on earth live our lives by the sun; and our solar day—that is, from noon to noon—is 24 hours.

The axis on which Mars spins to provide the day is not pointed to the same part of the sky as is the axis of the earth. The axes of the two planets are inclined to the planet paths around the sun by almost the same amount, but in spite of this they are about 35 degrees apart. Polaris, at the end of the handle of the Little Dipper, is our pole star and is less than one and a fourth degrees from the north celestial pole. Thus when we find Polaris, we have found our direction. A space traveler on Mars would not be so fortunate. The nearest star to the Martian north celestial pole is Alpha Cephei, which is a second magnitude star eight degrees north. The first magnitude star Alpha Cygni (Deneb) is ten degrees south of the pole.

A space traveler familiar with the sky of the earth and its circling around Polaris may find the skies quite strange and the motions of the stars disconcerting.

The Motions of Mars

The explanations of the motions of the planets in general and Mars in particular began a long time ago. In 1560 the fabulous Tycho Brahe, the 14-year-old son of a Danish nobleman, found himself attracted to astronomy by the fulfillment of a prediction of an eclipse. Overcoming the scruples of his highborn position, he became a distinguished astronomer and indeed so renowned that King Frederick II of Denmark established an observatory on the island of Hven, near Elsinore, for his use. Tycho was made financially independent by being given the income from the properties of the island. The observatory was furnished with the finest instruments available at that time. However, the telescope had not yet been invented—in fact, was not to be invented until after his death—and Tycho's first class instruments by our standards would be the crudest imaginable.

Even with these instruments Tycho made a 20-year series of accurate observations on the stars and planets which were the greatest contribution to observational astronomy up to that time. These observations were destined to play a major role in the establishment of that branch of astronomy—celestial mechanics—which treats of the motions of the heavenly bodies.

When Tycho neglected his duties as a landlord, the new boy king, through his advisors, scolded Tycho, who left not only Hven but Denmark as well. He went to Germany and eventually went to live in Prague in old Bohemia, where he became the official astronomer of the Holy Roman Emperor, Rudolph II.

At that time there lived an ingenious, sensitive young man in Prague who also had an interest in astronomy and who busied himself attempting to explain the harmonies and rhythmic relationships between the motions of the planets and why there were six planets. In fact, this very interest led him to the door of Tycho Brahe, and quite naturally Johann Kepler became Tycho's pupil as had many others before him. But Kepler was destined to eclipse his teacher and become one of the most distinguished astronomers of all time.

After the death of Tycho Brahe the tremendous volume of observations which had been amassed by Tycho Brahe and his staff was bequeathed to Kepler. From these observations Kepler resolved to find the explanations for how the planets move.

From the wealth of observations Kepler chose to investigate Mars, probably because it was the swiftest moving of the superior planets. For many years he tried without success to find combinations of circles which would fit the observations made by Tycho. Only when Kepler boldly discarded the idea that the perfect curve was a circle, only when he chose for the path of Mars the slightly flattened circle which mathematicians call an ellipse, did he succeed in predicting the future positions of Mars as well as in satisfying the previous observations of Tycho. In 1609 he announced his first and second laws of planetary motions, and by 1618 the third of the unifying laws had been established. To arrive at his laws he made innumerable wrong guesses and took six years of tedious, incessant calculation. Even his mysticism aided him in arriving at the third law. It led him to obtain a relation between the size of the orbit and the period of revolution.

1. Each planet moves in an ellipse which has the sun at one of its foci.
2. The radius vector of each planet passes over equal areas in equal intervals of time.

3. The cubes of the mean distances of any two planets from the sun are to each other as the squares of their periods.

With the above laws the motions of Mars can be understood. To begin, Mars moves in an orbit which is elliptical. There are many different forms of ellipses, varying from those which are very like circles to those which look like a plate seen almost edge on. In the case of Mars the orbit deviates from a circle by about 9 per cent in shape. The planets Pluto and Mercury have the greatest eccentricity of the planets in the solar system with 0.249 and 0.205. Mars comes next with an eccentricity of 0.0933. We have measured the distance between Mars and the sun at perihelion, when they are closest, and at aphelion, when they are farthest apart. These figures are respectively 129,000,000 and 154,000,000 miles. When the difference between them is divided by their sum, we get 0.0933, which is the eccentricity of the orbit. This makes the average distance of Mars from the sun about 141,500,000 miles, which is a little more than one and a half times the distance from the earth to the sun. Using this value and the length of the Martian year, we find that the average speed of the planet in its orbit around the sun is 54,000 miles per hour. Mars, farther from the sun, has a slower orbital speed than the 66,600 miles per hour for the earth.

When these distances are correlated with those of the earth, we find at the most favorable opposition the distance of Mars from earth is 34,600,000 miles. In 1924 the minimum distance was almost realized, for in that year Mars was 34,700,000 miles away. At the most unfavorable opposition the distance is 62,900,000 miles. The 1948 op-

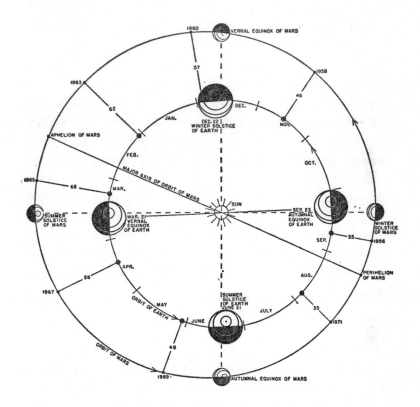

The orbits of the earth and Mars, as seen from the north pole of the sky, showing the near approach of the two planets. Notice that only those oppositions which occur in the fall are the close ones, for that is when Mars is at perihelion. (*Courtesy of Dr. C. H. Cleminshaw,* Griffith Observer)

position, in February, yielded the maximum distance. Favorable opposition occurs at intervals of 15 or 17 years.

Let's see how this evolves:

The sidereal year—that is, the time it takes Mars to go from one star in the sky around the sun and back to that star—is about 687 days, or about one year and ten months in length. However unless we are astronomers, we are not interested in the sidereal period. We are interested in that time at which Mars can be seen to best advantage. Therefore we are interested in the synodic period. This may be defined by the time when Mars is in the south at midnight to the next time it arrives at this same position. Obviously the motion of the earth enters into this period. When the simple calculation is performed, using the year of both Mars and the earth, we find that the synodic period is 780 days, or about two years and 50 days. If we divide this 50 into the 365 days of the terrestrial year, we get a factor of slightly more than seven. This means that favorable oppositions will occur in about that many Martian synodic periods.

Seasons

In the formation of the solar system, perhaps 5000 million years ago, the axes of some of the planets were tipped to their paths around the sun. Some of the axes were barely tipped at all, and so a planet like Jupiter circles the sun with it axis almost perpendicular to the plane of the orbit. On the other extreme there is the planet Uranus, whose axis is tipped 98 degrees. In the case of the earth the axis was tilted 23½ degrees.

In the northern hemisphere we have our summer season when the North Pole is tipped toward the sun. Taking a specific date, June 21 or the beginning of summer, the sun is seen highest in the sky at noon. For that reason it is also above the horizon for the longest period of time, the combination giving us hot weather. Six months later the North Pole is tipped away from the sun. For this reason the sun does not rise high in the sky, nor is it above the horizon for a long period of time; this results in cold weather. So every year the earth swings through its cycle of seasons—spring, summer, autumn, and finally winter—all because at the very dawn of time the axis of the earth was tipped. At that same long-ago time the axis of Mars was tipped about 25 degrees, ten minutes, to its path around the sun. Therefore Mars, like the earth, should also have seasons, and it does.

Mars, as we have discovered, moves in a highly eccentric orbit. Therefore when seasons come to Mars, they are not of almost equal lengths like those on the earth but vary considerably. In the case of the earth we are nearest to the sun, at perigee, in the winter—at which time the earth, obeying the Keplerian Law of Areas, moves fastest. The earth moves more slowly in the summer—when it is most distant from the sun, at aphelion. In a normal year the period from spring to summer is 93 days; from summer to autumn, 93 days; from autumn to winter, 90 days; from winter to spring, 89 days. If the year is divided into halves, there are 186 days in the spring and summer, when the earth is at aphelion. There are only 179 days in the fall and winter, when the earth is at perihelion. From this it is seen that the seasons on the earth are almost of equal length and the halves are not too dissimilar. Now let's examine the conditions in the case of Mars.

To begin, the year on Mars is 687 days in length, almost double that of the earth; therefore the seasons should also be almost double. However, with the orbit so eccentric, it is almost a certainty that the variation in seasons will be considerable. When Mars is at perihelion, it always has the South Pole tipped toward the sun. As Mars is moving rapidly at this time, the southern summer should be short. This is precisely the case. The southern summer or northern winter is 160 days in length. The southern autumn or northern spring is 199 days in length. The southern winter or northern summer is 182 days in length, and the southern spring or northern autumn is 146 days in length. These are measured in 24-hour days.

In the case of the earth the maximum spread between seasons is four days; on Mars it is 53 days. There is a 4 per cent time difference between the equinoxes for the earth, while in the case of Mars this difference is more than five times as much.

Since the southern summer occurs at perihelion, the southern summer is the hottest as well as the shortest season. This fact also explains the characteristic difference in the extent of the two polar caps of the planet. The southern winter is not only the coldest but the longest. This accounts for the excessive size of the southern polar cap. Likewise, the hot southern summer can shrink down the polar cap until it almost disappears. Climate in the southern hemisphere is extreme.

The northern hemisphere of Mars enjoys less extreme climate. Summer in the northern hemisphere takes place at aphelion, when the planet is farthest from the sun. This change in distance of 26 million miles is not too much when compared to the total distance, to affect the insolation—that is, the energy received from the sun.

From the researches of Hess it is concluded that there is a striking resemblance between the climatic variations on Mars and those on the earth. He attributes it to the close correspondence of rates of rotation, inclination of axis, presence of atmosphere, etc. Offsetting these are several factors which operate to negate the resemblance. These are the absence of high mountains and oceans, the extremely low water-vapor content of the Martian atmosphere. The greater uniformity of the Martian surface should also contribute to a pronounced regularity in weather. Again this is abetted by the lack of water vapor in the atmosphere with its erratic interference with incoming and outgoing radiation. Due to the length of the Martian year the temperature contrasts between the winter and summer should be greater than on the earth, as is apparent, and the long seasons on Mars should promote the exchange of air between the hemispheres. Let's look closely at these effects and their influence on the Martian climate.

Climate and Temperatures

On the earth climate is intimately associated with the air temperature. There is little change in temperature between the surface and the contiguous overlying air blanket. However, it can be shown that the temperature of the ground layer of air on Mars can be about 50 degrees F. colder than the surface which is accepted as a fundamental characteristic of the Martian climate. This differential in temperature should give rise to strong vertical currents, and indeed these have been observed. Also some idea of temperature distribution in the atmosphere can be obtained.

If an average daily temperature of 32 degrees F. is assumed for the surface in the equatorial regions, by the time we have ascended six miles the temperature has dropped to about −70 degrees F. At nine miles the temperature is −110 degrees F., and at 12 miles the temperature has dropped to −150 degrees F. Astronomers believe that theoretically the temperature should drop even lower at higher altitudes until it reaches a frigid −250 degrees F.

Actually the determination of temperatures is a difficult problem. It requires the extraordinary skillful handling of a telescope and a radiometer placed at its focus. The receiving element of the radiometer can be made quite minute so that even in a moderate telescope where the image of Mars may be about one eighth of an inch in diameter, this element can cover less than a tenth of the Martian disk— which means that essentially we are measuring the energy from areas on Mars which are 400 miles across.

What is obtained by the receiver is the combined long-wave planetary radiation and the reflected short-wave solar radiation. A fortuitous set of circumstances makes these two radiations fall in different parts of the spectrum. By interposing a water cell in the system, the long-wave radiation is absorbed and only the short-wave energy captured and measured. The difference represents the energy emitted by the planet; and by using well-understood mathematical procedures, the temperature can be computed. While this is the essence of the method, it is not without complications. The atmosphere of the earth will affect what passes through it, and even the atmosphere of Mars, as tenuous as it is, may have some bearing on the problem.

The result obtained by the water-cell transmission method, whose validity has been confirmed, still has to be corrected by having about 18 degrees F. added to it in order to yield the ground temperature. This correction eliminates the atmospheric influence. Appropriate techniques have been developed which yield consistent results and which merit considerable confidence.

Mean temperatures of the entire planet have been determined by setting the image of the planet on a receiver larger than the planetary disk. An average surface temperature of −90 degrees F. is found which takes into account the diurnal variation and the distance to the sun. The average yearly temperature on Mars is 65 degrees F. lower than that on the earth because of the greater distance of Mars from the sun. While −9 degrees F. is the average temperature for the entire planet, actually—as on the earth —different regions will possess different temperatures.

The polar regions will be colder than the mean. The equatorial regions will be warmer than the mean. The color of the surface also influences the temperature. For instance, dark objects will absorb solar radiation and so become warmer; light ones will reflect this radiation and not be heated so much. Radiometric measures on the bright and dark areas at the center of the disk and directly below the sun indicate that the dark areas are on the average about 16 degrees F. warmer than the adjacent bright areas. By the same token when the sun goes below the horizon, the darker areas—being warmer—will emit the accumulated energy faster than the other areas and so the temperature drop will be greater.

As we have seen, the eccentricity of the orbit of Mars varies the solar distance from 129,000,000 miles at perihelion to 154,000,000 miles at aphelion. This produces a change of about 50 degrees F. at the same subsolar point at these two times, due to the difference in the intensity of solar radiation received. The amount of solar energy falling on Mars at these two times varies by the ratio of 3 to 2, or by 50 per cent. On earth the variation is less than 7 per cent.

There is also a daily variation in temperature due to the rotation of the planet. The high for the day takes place between 12:30 and 1:00 P.M. and the low for the night takes place just before sunrise and is −100 degrees F. In the equatorial regions a variation of 60 degrees F. is the average. The highest diurnal temperature for the earth comes after 2:00 P.M. so that Mars appears to behave quite differently. The thinness of the Martian atmosphere is responsible for the absence of an appreciable lag in the daily temperatures.

At the 1954 opposition Mt. Palomar observers used a Golay detector, a small complex apparatus that depends on the expansion of a volume of gas under the influence of radiation, on the 200-inch Hale telescope to measure temperatures on the Martian surface. While there are many difficult problems associated with the operation of this device, the results merit its use. The findings yielded by the Golay detector substantiated results obtained by other means.

The extreme thinness of the atmosphere also precludes an appreciable seasonal lag. The yearly maximum temperature for the southern hemisphere should come at the summer solstice with no lag at all, while for the northern hemisphere there may be a lag of about 30 days. In the polar regions the lowest temperatures should come just before the equinoxes, while at the equator the extremes of temperature are determined by the solar distance.

Now to see the Martian seasonal picture in its entirety, let us choose the middle of summer in the southern hemisphere. The noon temperature at the South Pole can occasionally get up to almost 32 degrees F., though an average of 20 degrees F. is indicated. As we go from the polar regions to the south temperate zone, the noon temperature will increase to about 60 degrees F.; and by the time the equator is reached, the temperature will have gone up to 85 degrees F. Now, crossing the equator, we come to the north temperate zone, where the temperature will drop to about 0 degrees F. Continuing north, we come to a point near the polar circle where the temperature will drop to −40 degrees F., and finally in the unobservable regions of the polar night the temperature may have dropped to −150 degrees F. Because of the eccentricity of the orbit the range of temperatures will be different when winter comes to the southern hemisphere.

From this it is seen that the climate of Mars is not impossibly different from that of the earth. It is more extreme. Indeed, de Vaucouleurs says, "We can justly say that the Martian climate is of an exaggerated continental type."

It is doubtful that an imagined race of Martians would experience temperatures as severe as those on the earth. For instance, in Verkoyansk in North Central Siberia the temperature drops to −96 degrees F. while in Death Valley it goes up to 140 degrees F. It is difficult to find a temperature this low on the daylight side of Mars except in the polar regions, and we would assume that the hypothetical and impossible Martians would stay close to the equator or at least in the temperate zones. In the latter the temperature runs from 30 to 85 degrees except for the night, when the temperature is quite low, −100 degrees F.

3

↑

The Moons of Mars

The Moons in History

Mars, today, has two moons. It always has had two moons, but until recently we were not aware of it. In fact, the discovery of the moons of Mars was actually the fulfillment of a most amazing piece of intelligent speculation. There is a tremendous fascination in this story.

Let's go back to 1610. Kepler, in a critique of Galileo's *Sidereal Messenger,* proposed that in view of the one moon of the earth and the four moons of Jupiter it would be reasonable to assume that Mars had two moons and Saturn either six or eight. Like many of the scientists of his time and before, Kepler was something of a mystic, and was much impressed by the rhythm of numerical sequences. For example, he would notice that, according to Galileo's knowledge:

Venus has 0 satellites   Mars has X
Earth has 1   Jupiter has 4

And he would supply 2 as the missing figure for Mars.

About a century later, in 1726, the renowned English
satirist Jonathan Swift wrote of the travels of one mythical
Lemuel Gulliver to remote parts of the world. In Chapter
III, in the "Voyage to Laputa," Swift writes:

> They have likewise discovered the lesser stars, or satel-
> lites, which revolve about Mars; whereof the innermost
> is distant from the center of the primary planet exactly
> three of his diameters, and the outermost, five; the for-
> mer revolves in the space of ten hours and the latter in
> twenty-one and a half; so that the squares of their period-
> ical times are very near in the same proportion with the
> cubes of their distance from the center of Mars; which
> evidently shows them to be governed by the same law
> of gravitation that influences the other heavenly bodies.

Undoubtedly Swift was influenced by Kepler's earlier
reasoning. He was a learned man and traveled in learned
company. He evidently knew how to interpret the Keplerian laws of planetary motion, and what he didn't know
or found difficult to comprehend could be interpreted by
his astronomical friends. The astronomy texts of that time
contained substantial amounts of planetary and satellite
data with which Swift could tinker. Given sufficient time
and imagination (of which he possessed much), Swift might
well have arrived independently at this conclusion. As we
shall presently see, while Swift did not precisely predict
periods and distances, the similarity between the hypothetical satellites and the real ones was so close that it remains
one of the most amazing feats of speculation.

The really incredible part of the speculation was in the
distances Swift chose. Of this Roscoe Lamont writes:

The reason why Swift took the distances of the moons from the earth's center of three of the earth's diameters diameter was probably this: He had read in David Gregory's astronomy, published in 1713 (Vol. I, page 25, of the second edition of 1726), the following about Jupiter's satellites: "Jupiter has four; the innermost of which revolves about in $1\frac{1}{4}$ of a day, at the distance of $5\frac{2}{3}$ semi-diameters of Jupiter from his center; the second revolves in $3\frac{1}{5}$ days at the distance of 9 semi-diameters." $5\frac{2}{3}$ and 9 semi-diameters are $2\frac{5}{6}$ and $4\frac{1}{2}$ diameters, so Swift took those of Mars as 3 and 5.

Or, having fixed the distance of the inner moon from the center of Mars at three diameters of the planet, Swift may have reasoned like this: A moon at a distance from Jupiter's center of about three of his diameters revolves in $1\frac{1}{4}$ of a day or 30 hours. A moon at a distance from the center of Mars as 3 and 5 times the planet's would revolve in about 20 hours (as he would find). So let's have a moon at a distance from the center of Mars of three of his diameters go around in ten hours.

Probably influenced by Jonathan Swift, Voltaire in 1752 wrote his *Micromegas,* in which he speaks of Mars and attributes to it two small satellites which are necessary to light (?) Mars and are too small to have been perceived by terrestrial astronomers. Even Cyrano de Bergerac "got into the act" with a prediction of Martian satellites.

This kind of speculation was not confined to lay writers and to mystics like Kepler. Even the rather sober astronomer Sir William Herschel once postulated that there were inhabitants of the sun, down below the brilliant hot layer that sends us our light and heat. And after Herschel discovered the planet Uranus, he predicted a system of rings surrounding it.

Here the reason was that the outermost naked eye planet in the solar system, Saturn, possessed a ring system and therefore the planet beyond it should also possess a thin system of rings which would pass through the plane of the earth. The fact that the rings were not seen did not negate the idea, for he realized that when the ring system of Saturn is turned edge-on, these rings, too, disappear at times. Also Herschel was beginning to appreciate the power and potentialities of larger telescopes and he believed that eventually a telescope large enough to observe this ring system would be built.

The Moons Are Discovered

In 1877 Asaph Hall, the Director of the Naval Observatory in Washington, had been observing with the 26-inch Clark refractor, one of the finest instruments ever erected. His mind ran to an investigation of the planet Mars and the possibility of its possessing satellites. He undertook a search of the literature trying to discover who last tried to find the possible satellites. His researches indicated that few astronomers had wasted any time on the satellites of Mars since Herschel had made a special search for this feature and had been unsuccessful. After failing to discover satellites, Herschel simply said that Mars possessed none, and thereafter the textbooks on astronomy published the fact that Mars did not have moons.

In 1862 Professor H. L. d'Arrest, director of the Copenhagen Observatory, may have made a search at the favorable opposition in that year. Historians are not certain about that but they are sure that two years later, in 1864, at an opposition which could not have been as favorable as the one in 1862, he did observe Mars carefully and assiduously but discovered no moons.

Asaph Hall saw in the close and memorable opposition of 1877 a chance to test the new telescope. One of the tasks he undertook was to determine the observational caliber of the telescope by using it in the search for the satellites. He began observing in early August of that year, beginning at a considerable distance from Mars. His first attempts were unsuccessful, but encouraged by his wife he continued his search and on August 11 he discovered the outer satellite. Several days later, on August 17, he discovered the inner satellite whose behavior puzzled him very much.

It moves so swiftly that he saw it on opposite sides of the planet after such short intervals that he thought for a while that perhaps Mars had two or three inner moons; it seemed to Hall very improbable that the inner moon could revolve around Mars in less than a day. But subsequent observations demonstrated the singularity of the satellite, and Hall announced that Mars had two moons. A Mr. Madan of Eton, England, suggested that, inasmuch as Mars was the god of war, the inner moon might be named Phobos—Fear—and the outer moon Deimos—Dread—in keeping with the parent body's reputation.

Not only are the satellites much fainter than many of those on Jupiter and Saturn but they are very close to the planet and are lost in its glare unless care is taken to "block out" the image of Mars. If the two objects were not so close to the planet, it would be comparatively easy to see them with even moderate telescopes. The astronomer characterizes the brightnesses of objects in terms of "magnitudes" and says that Phobos is of magnitude 12, while Deimos is 13. Translating this into more familiar terms, we can say that if Deimos were 700 times brighter, it would be just visible to the naked eye under ideal conditions, if Mars were not present to flood the telescope with light.

The satellites are too small to permit their real sizes to be determined. They appear to be tiny points even in large telescopes. The astronomer assumes that they reflect light in the same way as Mars does—an assumption with which not all scientists are in agreement—and then determines their sizes from their apparent brightnesses. Phobos, the inner moon, turns out to be the larger, with a diameter of about ten miles; Deimos has a diameter of about five miles—a chunk of rock about the size of Mt. Everest. If the satellites are better reflectors of light than Mars, they must necessarily be smaller than the figures we have just suggested; if they are poorer reflectors, they must be bigger.

To discover them, Asaph Hall had to keep Mars just outside the field of his telescope, and later observers have used the same technique to study the satellites. Antoniadi at Meudon, France, studied them carefully, and concluded that they differ markedly in color from Mars. To him Phobos appeared white, while Deimos had a bluish cast. He likened these colors to some he had observed in the asteroids, the little planetoids that revolve around the sun in orbits between Mars and Jupiter.

Phobos, the inner satellite, moves swiftly around the

planet in 7 hours, 39 minutes (compare Swift's 10 hours). While their orbits are elliptical, they are of low eccentricity. The mean distance of Phobos from the center of Mars is 5826 miles; this means that it is only about 3701 miles from the surface of the planet, about the distance from New York to Nome, Alaska. Deimos is 14,580 miles from the center of Mars and 12,455 miles above the surface. For comparison, we might recall that our moon revolves at a mean distance of 239,000 miles from the center of the earth.

The periods of these satellites are the shortest known in our whole system. The period of Phobos is less than a third of the rotation period of Mars. Because it moves faster than the surface of Mars, this satellite rises in the west and sets in the east. From one rising of Phobos to the next the interval is only 11 hours, 7 minutes; from rising to setting, the interval is 4¼ hours.

The behavior of Deimos is quite different. The rotation period of the planet is about 24 hours, 37 minutes, while the period of Deimos is 30 hours, 18 minutes, so little more than the "day" of Mars that the satellite appears to hang almost stationary in the Martian sky. It stays above the horizon more than 60 hours, and requires about 132 hours to make one trip around the planet, as seen from some fixed location on Mars. For about two and a half days it is above the horizon, then for almost another three days it is below and invisible.

The orbits of the satellites do not lie in the plane of the planet's equator but are, instead, slightly inclined to it. The nodes of these orbits—the points where the paths intersect the plane of the planet's equator—are not stationary,

but due to the bulge of the planet's equator they retrograde. The nodes of Phobos slip all the way around once
in two and a half years; those of Deimos have a period of
56 years.

As seen from the surface of Mars, these satellites would
appear far less conspicuous than our moon appears to us.
Our moon on the average is 239,000 miles from the surface
of the earth, and its diameter is about 2160 miles, so its
distance is about 110 times its diameter. That makes it
appear to be of a certain angular diameter, about half a
degree. Now let's look at Phobos, which is only ten miles
in diameter and 3700 miles from the surface of Mars. Its
distance is 370 times its diameter and it must therefore
appear smaller than our moon does to us. Its angular
diameter is less than a third of that of our moon. It would
still be quite bright—about a sixtieth as bright as our
moon—and its phases would be easily seen.

But Deimos is only five miles in diameter, and its distance of 12,455 miles from the surface of Mars is almost
2500 times its diameter. As a result this outer satellite
would appear from Mars to have a diameter about one
twenty-fourth of the diameter of our moon as seen by us.
This is too small for phases to be readily perceived with
the naked eye, so Deimos would appear to be a bright
star in the Martian sky, varying in brightness as it passes
through its phases. Even at the full phase Deimos would
be only 1/200 as bright as our moon.

There is an interesting overtone to the smallness of these
moons. When space travel materializes and men travel to
Mars, they will not land directly on the surface of the
planet but may, following the von Braun proposal, circle

the planet or, what is more likely, land on one of the satellites. These could serve as bases or space stations because of their tiny size and low gravitational powers. A space traveler exploring one of these moons would not dare leap upward. To do so would be to escape from the feeble gravitation and go sailing off into space.

The nearness of the satellites to the surface precludes their being seen from the entire planet. From latitudes greater than 69½ degrees—corresponding to a place just south of Point Barrow, Alaska, on earth—the inner moon Phobos could not be seen; it would always be below the horizon. Similarly Deimos the outer satellite could not be seen in latitudes greater than 82½ degrees. Actually these are theoretical limits for an atmosphereless planet; even a very thin atmosphere would dim the moons so they couldn't be seen right at the horizon, so effectively the regions from which the moons could be seen are somewhat more restricted than indicated above.

From the middle belt of the planet the view of the moons of Mars would be an interesting one, and quite different from what we on earth enjoy with our one moon. The eclipses of the sun and of the Martian satellites would be hard to keep up with. The phases of Phobos, the inner satellite, would be easily seen, but neither satellite can ever be seen in the full phase, because they both are too close to the planet and pass through its shadow each time around.

On earth when the moon passes directly in front of the sun and completely hides the bright disk, revealing the corona, we have one of the most spectacular sights in nature—the total eclipse. From any one spot on earth this can be observed on the average only once in about 400 years. Both partial eclipses—in which the moon passes above or below the center of the sun, leaving a crescent visible at maximum—and annular eclipses—in which the moon crosses the center of the sun but leaves a thin ring or annulus of sunlight—occur more often.

Eclipses of the moon, produced when our satellite passes through the shadow of the earth, occur less often than solar eclipses, but picture the situation on Mars. In any one night of, say, 12 hours, it is possible to see three eclipses, two of Phobos and one of Deimos. In the course of a Martian year there may be as many as 1400 eclipses of Phobos and 130 eclipses of Deimos! Compare this with a maximum of three eclipses of our moon in a single year. Under rare conditions both moons of Mars may be in eclipse at one time.

But Mars would not be exactly an astronomer's paradise as far as eclipses of the sun are concerned. True, there are far more of them than on earth, but the quality is far below ours. From the earth the moon and the sun appear to be of just about the same size, so the moon can cover all of the sun's disk, to produce the spectacularly beautiful phenomenon of a total eclipse. The satellites of Mars are very small and never entirely cover the sun's disk, even when we consider that the sun, from Mars, appears to have only two thirds of its diameter as seen from earth. Phobos, as seen from the surface of Mars, has a diameter about one half that of the sun, so the best we could hope for would be an annular eclipse. The outer satellite, Deimos, is so much farther away and so much smaller that it would be seen only as a small black object transiting the sun.

On earth a total eclipse of the sun can last for a maximum of about 450 seconds. On Mars, because the satellites move so fast, Phobos takes only 19 seconds to cross the sun's face, while the duration for Deimos would be only about 108 seconds.

Despite the smallness of Deimos an intriguing fact about it has been learned. Like our own moon this small satellite of Mars seems to keep one face turned always toward its primary. This has been determined by measuring the brightness of the satellite at various times and finding that when it is on one side of the planet it is brighter than when on the other side. This seems to be a more or less universal characteristic of satellites that are close to more massive bodies. Antoniadi found this true of the eighth satellite of Saturn and the first and third of Jupiter; it is true also of the planet Mercury, which keeps one face turned always toward the sun.

Mars, as seen from the satellites, would present a remarkable spectacle. As seen from Phobos, the planet would subtend an angle of about 42 degrees, or 84 times the apparent diameter of our moon. With the edge of Mars on the horizon, the planet would extend almost halfway up to the zenith; its apparent area would be more than 7000 times as great as that of our moon. What a conversation piece we would have on earth if our moon loomed that large. Because Phobos is so close to the planet, only about half of a hemisphere—an area only 137 degrees across—could be seen at one time, and the surface of the planet would noticeably bulge toward the satellite and would be enlarged with respect to the rim of the visible area.

As seen from Deimos, Mars subtends only 16 degrees— 32 times the diameter of our moon as seen by us—and the area is more than 1000 times the apparent area of our moon as we see it. From Deimos, the inner satellite Phobos would appear to go through all of the phases of our moon, except that just as it approaches full phase it would appear to go into eclipse in the shadow of Mars.

Space expeditions of the future, with Mars as the target, should, and probably will, land on one of the satellites first. Either one, but particularly Phobos, would provide an ideal temporary platform from which you may study the surface of Mars in great detail before landing on the planet itself.

4

The Face of Mars

On July 27, 1939, Mars was only slightly more than 36,000,000 miles from the earth. The favorable opposition brought forth considerable newspaper and radio comment about the "red planet," and there was keen interest in Mars among the public. Visitors flocked in great numbers to look at Mars through any telescope that could be made available to them.

In the Museum of The Franklin Institute, located in the heart of Philadelphia, is a public observatory housing two large telescopes, one of which is ideally suited to planetary observations. Magnifying powers up to 750 diameters can be used with this instrument, although the disturbed air above the city seldom permits a magnification of more than 300 times.

On one August night the seeing was superb. The day had been quite warm, and even four hours after sunset the air was warm and humid. The fainter stars could not be seen through the slight haze, but the brighter ones shone as steadily as beacons. On such nights seeing is sometimes

51

very good, and on this occasion a magnifying power of 750 diameters was used to observe Mars.

The view of the bright polar caps is still memorable. The disk of the planet loomed as a dull-orange ball with darker markings here and there, and always there was a feeling that just beyond what was seen there was much more to be seen. Occasionally there would come an instant of super-seeing and the evanescent straight-line markings—the famous canals—would flash into view, only to disappear as suddenly as they had come, leaving one with a helpless sense of frustration. If only the super-seeing could have persisted for a second or two at a time, and more frequently, one could be more certain of the reality of the canals and of their positions and number. As it was, only the strong memory of the polar caps, the orange ball with darker areas, and a feeling of tantalizing detail beyond them persists.

This experience of frustration is by no means unique. Thousands of observers in the past three centuries and more have been similarly bedeviled. It was inevitable that Galileo should have turned his newly invented telescope toward Mars, in 1610, to see markings there. No known drawings of this planet by Galileo exist, unfortunately, but shortly afterward there were other observers who did make telescopic drawings.

In 1639 the Italian astronomer François Fontana possessed a telescope so much improved over the primitive instruments of Galileo that he was able to sketch some Martian detail, and by 1659 the Dutch observer Huygens was able to follow the dark markings so well that he an-

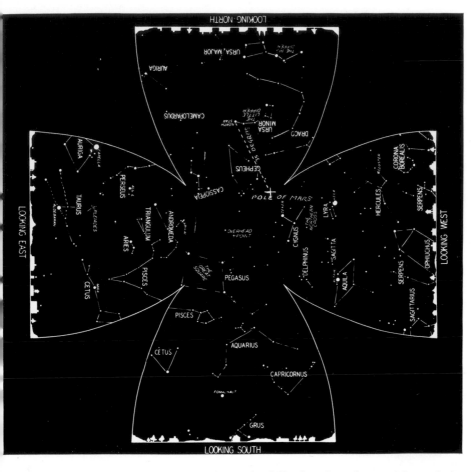

Map of the sky in early fall, showing the position of the Martian north celestial pole. Notice it is almost between the brightest star in Cepheus and the brightest star in Cygnus. The two poles are separated by 35°. (*Courtesy of Star Maps for Beginners*)

One of the finest photographs of Mars. The south polar cap can be seen at the top of the picture. Circling Mars is a belt of greenish areas. The daggerlike marking going down and to the right is the Syrtis Major.

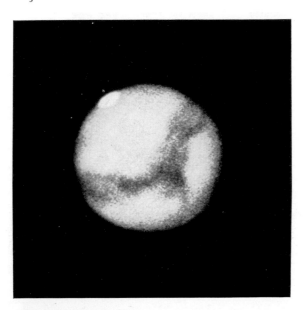

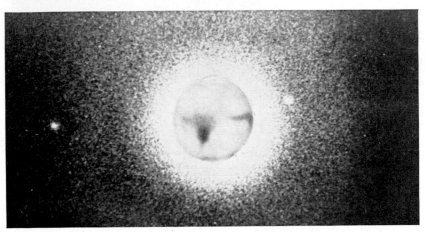

A composite photograph (August 17, 1924) showing Mars and the two satellites. *(Courtesy of E. C. Slipher, Lowell Observatory)*

Photograph and drawing of Mars (October 22, 1926). The difference in what the photograph shows and what the human eye can see is clearly visible.

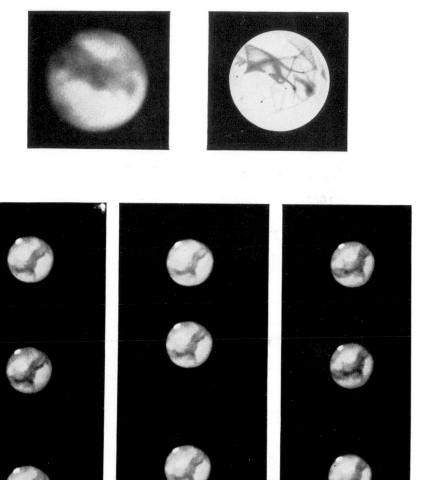

These nine photographs of the Syrtis Major region (September 28, 1909) show the changes caused by the rotation of the planet: 22 minutes elapsed between the first and second columns and one hour between the second and third columns.

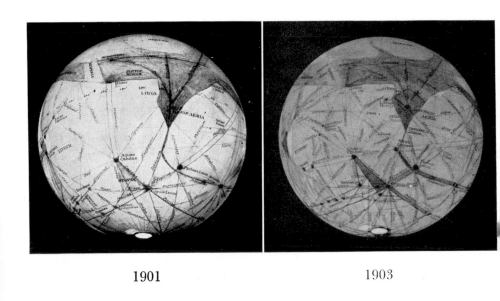

1901   1903

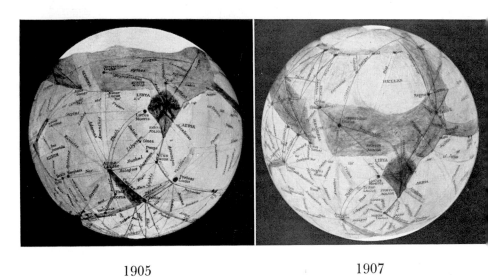

1905   1907

Lowell globes of Mars showing the increase of detail over a period of six years. (*Courtesy of E. C. Slipher, Lowell Observatory*)

This wash drawing, about 15 inches in diameter, was made by Simon Newcomb to test integrating properties of the observer's eye. Note the splotches that have been placed along lines to permit the eye to follow the pattern.

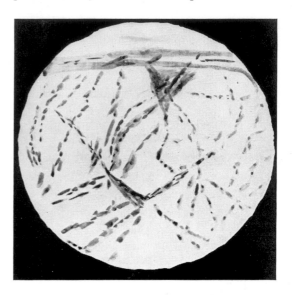

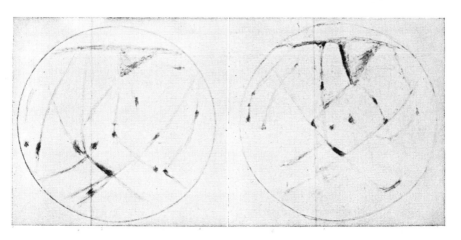

These drawings were made by E. E. Bernard and Philip Fox, two of the keenest-eyed observers of their time. While splotches are indicated, lines have been added to make linear detail.

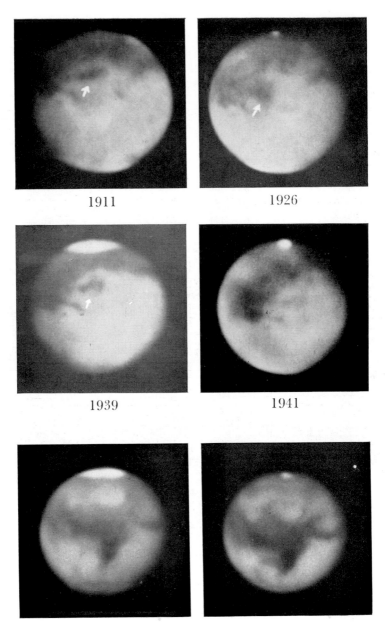

1911   1926

1939   1941

These photographs of Mars show the changes in the Solis Lacus. The two pictures at the bottom of the page show the Syrtis Major in the spring (1939) at left and in the summer (1941) at right. (*All courtesy of E. C. Slipher, Lowell Observatory*)

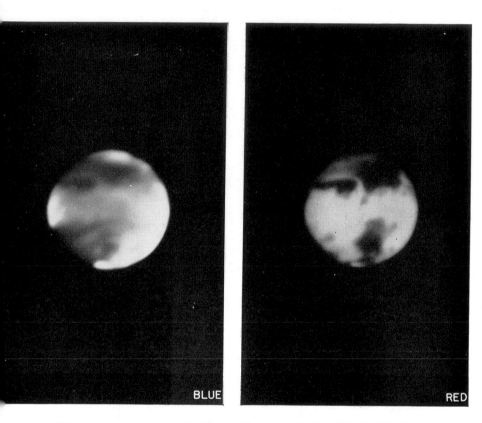

These two pictures of Mars, photographed with the 200-inch Hale telescope in blue and red lights, show the penetrating power of the red light to reveal surface detail.

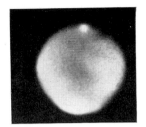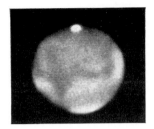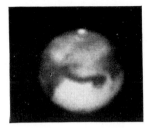

Blue clouds on Mars, above, apparent in the two left-hand photographs, disappear in yellow light, in the right-hand picture. In the series of pictures below, Mars, in yellow light, shows seasonal changes on planet (1941). *(All courtesy of E. C. Slipher, Lowell Observatory)*

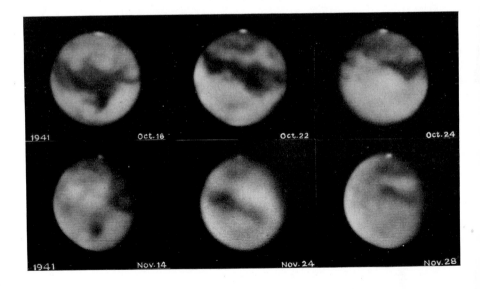

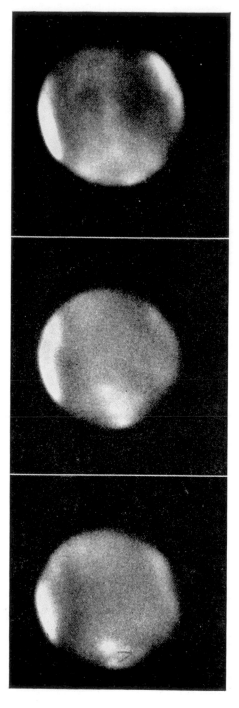

Three blue-light photographs of Mars were taken by E. C. Slipher in South Africa. On the left and center photographs are seen the W-shaped cloud formation that re-formed each afternoon on the planet. These were taken on June 20 and 26. The right-hand photograph was taken in the same region, but on the morning side, and there is no trace of this peculiar cloud. The left-hand picture has a dark line drawn in by an artist to show the outline of the W.

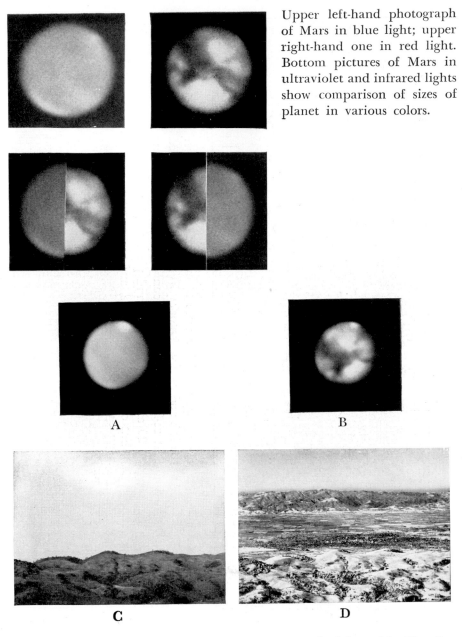

Upper left-hand photograph of Mars in blue light; upper right-hand one in red light. Bottom pictures of Mars in ultraviolet and infrared lights show comparison of sizes of planet in various colors.

A

B

C

D

Mars and San Jose (13½ miles distant) photographed from Mt. Hamilton: A and C in violet, B and D in infrared. The obliteration in C is due to earth's atmosphere, and the comparison is suggestive of the presence of an atmosphere of considerable density on Mars.

The Great Nebula in Orion: In the heart of this gaseous mass two new stars have been discovered in the past seven years. For the first time in the history of astronomy the birth of stars has been witnessed.

This is a star cloud in Sagittarius. In this cloud are found little dark patches of obscuring gases and dust called globules. Some astronomers believe that stars are born by the action of radiation pressure on the clouds.

Here is the great galaxy in Andromeda, one similar to the Milky Way. It, too, contains billions of stars, star clusters, variable stars, obscuring clouds, and other features common to our Milky Way. It is one of the nearest in the sky, being about 1.5 million light-years away.

The great galaxy in Canes Venatici is seen broadside on.
It shows the spiral structure of the galaxy. This one is about
four million light-years away.

The Corona Borealis cluster of galaxies. Each of the fuzzy patches in this photograph is a galaxy containing billions of stars.

nounced that the rotation period of Mars was about the same as that of the earth.

Observers for the next two centuries after Huygens added details and discriminated between several different types of markings. There were the brilliant whitish markings seen at the poles of the planet, today recognized as polar caps composed of hoarfrost. There were the bright predominating reddish-ocher areas covering about two thirds of the planet; these give Mars the color that is seen with the unaided eye, as well as the name of the "red planet." There were darker areas appearing to undergo erratic or progressive changes in some instances and in others appearing to be precisely correlated with the progress of the seasons on Mars. Evanescent markings identified as clouds of various types were seen, some persisting for short times, others for extended periods. Finally the subtle straight-line markings, at the critical limit of visibility with large telescopes and ideal seeing conditions, were seen and were called canals, thus touching off the most controversial topic in all astronomy. Let's examine these features in detail.

The Bright Areas

The reddish areas of Mars had been observed assiduously through the first three quarters of the nineteenth century, but at the favorable opposition of 1877 Giovanni Schiaparelli of Milan noticed that these "continents," as he thought of them, were by no means of uniform color. While it was true that the dusky red or orange color prevailed over the bulk of the areas, some minor regions showed variations ranging from white through yellow to a darker red.

If these brighter areas were the continents, the darkest areas must be the seas. But there were some regions which Schiaparelli could consider neither land nor sea, so he thought of them as swamp areas whose variations in color were caused by variations in the depth of water. Schiaparelli was never to know that there is a complete lack of free water on the surface of Mars; it remained for Percival Lowell in the 1890's to discover complex detail in the dark areas that completely denies the possibility that seas exist on Mars.

Lowell regarded the red areas as deserts comparable to the Painted Desert in Arizona or to the Sahara Desert in Northern Africa, but planet-wide in extent. In essence they are naked, arid, barren zones of sterile rock formations that completely girdle the planet, regions where no vegetation could grow. Further, Lowell saw in Mars the earth at some distant future date when the earth would have lost its water, the lush green areas would have given way to the inexorable sweep of the deserts, and finally a desperate battle to survive would be waged by the remaining population. All of this was based on the premise that the red areas are deserts, with no vegetation, no water —just bleak, unbroken tracts of sand.

Since the advent of this Lowell hypothesis many have attempted to discover just what the surface of Mars is like. Rupert Wildt in 1934 thought of the bright areas as sandy formations whose iron content had been completely oxidized, or rusted, so that great quantities of iron oxide exist. This single hypothesis could simultaneously account for the ruddy color of the disk and for the scarcity of oxygen in the atmosphere of the planet.

There was a certain nebulous attractiveness in the concept of Mars as a "rusted" planet. It could imply the existence, in the remote past, of an oxygen-rich atmosphere of biological origin. For this reason many eminent astronomers at that time embraced the idea, but this premise had no objective proof and only within the past few years has there been advanced a satisfactory theory of the origin and evolution of an atmosphere. But regardless of the mechanism by which the red areas came into being, could the nature of the surface somehow be discerned?

When light is reflected from a surface, it is to some extent polarized. That is, the waves of light, instead of vibrating in all possible planes, vibrate only in one plane, or in several planes close to each other. Various materials and various textures of surfaces will yield various degrees of polarization. During the 1922, 1924, and 1926 oppositions of Mars the French astronomer Dr. Bernard Lyot, using the 33-inch refractor at the Observatory of Paris at Meudon, France, succeeded in obtaining accurate measurements of the polarized light from various areas of Mars. He found that his measures bore a striking resemblance to those obtained from studies of the moon's surface. There was a variation from year to year, but it was not too pronounced.

From several lines of study we believe that the surface of the moon is covered with at least a thin layer of dust composed of something that reflects light like volcanic ash, and Lyot succeeded in obtaining polarization curves for mixtures of gray, brownish, and bluish volcanic ash that matched the curves for Mars tolerably well.

With a completely different approach to the problem, and using the 82-inch reflector at the McDonald Observatory in Texas, Dr. Gerard P. Kuiper measured the intensities of the absorption lines in the infrared spectra of Mars and the moon. While these two did not match precisely, the measures for Mars duplicated throughout the visible and infrared regions of the spectrum the curve for a brown rock, felsite, composed principally of aluminum and potassium silicate. This is an igneous rock—one formed as a result of volcanic activity or a similar mechanism—so again an igneous origin for the materials of the bright areas was suggested.

Further, W. W. Coblentz measured the intensity of the energy reflected from Mars in various regions of the spectrum and concluded that in a narrow band in the infrared there was an effect that matched the behavior of silicates or silicate debris like sand.

Here we have three different avenues of research leading to compatible results. Now we should be all set to say that a rock or sand based on silicon compounds composes the surface. But it is not that easy.

More recently Dr. A. Dollfus, a pupil of Dr. Lyot, again carried out observations of the polarization of the light reflected from Mars. Using the 24-inch refractor of France's high altitude observatory on Pic du Midi in the Southern Pyrenees, Dr. Dollfus obtained an excellent polarimetric curve fully corrected for the effects of the thin atmosphere above the observatory. This curve was compared with those from hundreds of terrestrial materials under a variety of conditions, and Dollfus found that the bright areas of Mars appear to possess the same characteristics as an irregular deposit of pulverized limonite, a brown iron ore.

Of this result Dr. Gerard de Vaucouleurs states: "The exact agreement between two highly peculiar curves, those of Mars and limonite, makes the method 'very specific' and the identification 'most critical' so that other possibilities seem excluded."

Here is, indeed, a dilemma. From infrared spectrum studies felsite appears to be the answer, while polarization studies tell us limonite. Certainly further studies appear to be in order, to decide which of these two, or some combination, or perhaps some very different material, will resolve this problem.

One possible explanation for the different conclusions may lie in the variation of the constitution of the top layer of Mars. There have been observed on Mars certain phenomena suggestive of volcanic eruptions; perhaps at certain times the surface has a heavier layer of igneous dust. There are winds on Mars, and dust storms, and these may carry one kind of dust or another from place to place, to confuse the picture. In any event a good identification of the nature of the Martian surface material appears imminent if this type of research is pursued with the giant telescopes.

The surface of Mars must be monotonously flat. Percival Lowell came to the conclusion that mountain peaks no higher than 2000 feet were present, but more recent observers feel that there could be peaks there from 6000 to

9000 feet high. This still falls far short of earth's Mount Everest, with its altitude of 29,000 feet.

When we observe the moon, we find the terminator, the line between the day and night side, quite rough and ragged. As the moon rotates, the top of a mountain peak catches the sunlight before the sides or foot of the mountain do, and so it should be on Mars as well. There should be irregularities at the sunrise or sunset lines of the planet, if mountains of any size are prevalent there, but the few scattered observations tell us that no mountains comparable to those on the moon or the earth exist there.

There is some evidence that the bright areas may be elevated tablelands rising perhaps 2000 feet above the dark regions. At certain times, and always at the same places, white spots become visible. These have been considered to be summits of isolated mountains temporarily covered with light snow or hoarfrost.

The Dark Areas

An intriguing explanation of the dark areas of Mars was proposed by Lowell, who considered the regularly repeating patterns of change on the surface of the planet to be the recurring growth of vegetation. But the changes came to be recognized as extremely complex and could not be dismissed simply as seasonal growth.

The Martian dark areas or "seas" are very different in shape and character from those on the moon. The lunar *"maria"* are essentially circular; the Martian counterparts are never circular. From this we can conclude that the formation mechanisms for the seas on these two bodies were different. The Martian seas tend to be elongated and to terminate in triangular or funnel-shaped "bays" or have such bays as tributaries.

The dark areas of the equatorial belt are nearly all south of the equator and point from southeast to northwest. Some of the strongest markings in the north equatorial belt, such as Thoth and Cerberus, follow this pattern. The most conspicuous dark pattern on Mars, Syrtis Major (Great Bog), which extends north of the equator, likewise follows this trend. Some astronomers believe that this curious systematic orientation of these elongated areas cannot be considered fortuitous.

The changes in the dark areas were recorded long ago. The closest opposition of Mars in the nineteenth century occurred in 1830, and at that time the German astronomers Wilhelm Beer and Johann Madler made the first systematic chart of the surface markings, publishing the first map of Mars in 1840. Other maps came along, and in them the convention was followed of calling the dark areas "seas" and the bright areas "continents."

The seasonal changes were at first obscured by the fact that we can see Mars throughout only eight earth months at a time, which corresponds to only three or four Martian months. At a single opposition, therefore, only a portion of the complete seasonal cycle can be observed. However, in years before and after the year of closest approach we can fill in the missing Martian months, but under less favorable conditions. By the turn of the last century the seasonal changes had become firmly established.

It became apparent that the growth of the dark areas was intimately associated with the shrinking of the polar

caps. The growth of the areas and their changes in color
led to the belief that the dark regions are covered with
vegetation that flourishes as the meager water supply of
Mars, largely locked up in the polar caps, is released by the
onset of summer.

There is a definite sequence to the cycle of changes.
Just after midsummer, when the snow at the South Pole of
Mars begins to shrink noticeably, the dusky, delicate markings in the immediate vicinity of the polar cap begin to
darken. As a wave, this darkening proceeds from the pole
to the equator at a variable rate, but sometimes in excess of
one mile per hour. Crossing the equator, it advances into
the low equatorial regions of the northern hemisphere,
where winter now prevails. Long before any considerable
decrease in size of the south polar cap, the wave of darkening has passed the equator. In late autumn the darkening
begins to fade; the areas are faintest soon after midwinter.

While this sounds like a simple change, actually its com-
plexities have never been completely resolved, because
the changes are not only of form but of color. The same
observers have seen the same areas of different colors in
the same phase of season at different oppositions. Further,
the changes in the equatorial region are complicated by the
fact that while one pole is melting, the other is building
up, and effects of both poles are present.

Comparisons of drawings over the years have revealed
substantial changes in some of the major dark areas of
Mars. The best-known example is Syrtis Major, the shape
of which today is different from that of the last century.
Most of the Martian features differ in some degree from
their appearances at former times, and there is no easy

explanation known today. However, it may be that the variable transparency of the Martian atmosphere may have some influence on the appearance of the surface markings from time to time.

One of the major changes has taken place in the northern hemisphere. A little below the center of the disk and to the left of Syrtis Major during the opposition of 1907 an almost featureless bright area existed. By 1939 there had developed a conspicuous dusky curved band, Thoth-Nepenthes. At the opposition of 1954 a huge dark region had developed, and Martian observers call this the greatest alteration in the surface features of Mars since it was first mapped 115 years earlier.

Mount Wilson photographs reveal this as a most surprising change. Between the 1952 and 1954 oppositions the Thoth-Nepenthes canal changed from a slightly dusky streak, almost of the normal orange-red color of the continents, to the dark colors of the seas, over an area twice as large as the island of Madagascar. At one time quite hard to see, Thoth-Nepenthes now is of such enhanced character that it can hardly more be classed as a canal. While the smaller and rather inconspicuous changes have been going on for some time in this area, the acceleration in only two years is remarkable, and it will be very interesting to see along what lines further development occurs.

Despite changes such as the one just described, the significant feature concerning the dark areas has been the cyclical change which has been the subject of serious and prolonged study. The most prominent and important work along this line must be attributed to Lowell and his colleagues at the turn of the century. Continuous observations at both favorable and distant oppositions, under the bright, clear skies of the Southwest and with the use of large telescopes, convinced these observers that the cyclic changes were due to quickening of the vegetation covering the dark areas.

It is not difficult to follow the thoughts of these early observers. First they saw the changes, which seemed to be in step with the seasons. The dark areas, a brownish, vague color at some times, grew darker as the season advanced from the onset of spring, and the color became greenish. As the autumn came on, the color changed back to brownish, and the areas became less conspicuous. The sequence was likened to the changes we observe on earth, where our plains and forests turn green with the advent of spring and summer, then turn reddish brown as autumn comes along. Some dark areas underwent little or no change on Mars, and these were likened to the prairies of earth, which change less than the wooded areas.

The darkening of the areas as the polar cap shrank was to these observers evidence of the release of water to vegetation hypersensitive to moisture. The farther a marking was from the pole, the later the darkening, which seemed evidence of seasonal changes directly associated with a physical agent proceeding from the pole and, as it were, exploding in all directions.

Lowell pointed out that the wave of quickening on Mars proceeds from the edge of the polar cap toward the equator, whereas on earth the direction is reversed; here the season advances from the equator toward the pole, then recedes in the opposite direction. But Lowell explained this by saying that on Mars the dependence was almost entirely on water, and until water could be released by the melting polar cap there could be no renewal of growth of vegetation. Then that growth would take place first where water was available earliest, and proceed from that region toward the equator.

From these observations and reasonings of the Lowell school of astronomers the idea spread among most others that vegetation in some form must be present on the surface of Mars. But there were some astronomers who asked questions and suggested that, if vegetation exists there, some tests should be possible that would disclose it. In a later chapter such tests and the conclusions from them will be described.

The Polar Caps

Some time in the future adventurous man will reach the moon. There he can gaze into the velvety black sky and see a magnificent sight—the spinning earth, much larger and brighter than the moon, hanging practically stationary in the sky, but slowly turning on its axis, once around each 24 hours, and passing through the same changes of phase each month, as we are accustomed to observe in the moon viewed from earth.

If our space traveler continues to watch the earth for a long time, he will be able to see the progression of the seasons. When winter comes to the northern hemisphere, he can watch the polar cap expand southward from the upper reaches of Canada until it reaches down into the northern fringe of the United States. As the immediate weather changes, the border of the polar cap will fluctuate somewhat, but in the middle or even southern part of Canada, in some winters, there will be a limit beyond which the cap will not retreat except with the coming of spring.

At the other end of the year the polar cap will have retreated to its minimum size, in the northern hemisphere, but snows will still be seen piled up in the arctic regions, while at the tip of South America there will be an extension of the always-present south polar cap.

Viewed from Mars, the earth will be far more difficult to observe; detailed changes in the polar caps will not be easy to see, but the seasonal changes will certainly not be missed. However, there is an important difference between the seasonal behavior of the polar caps of earth and those of Mars. Ours, here at home, never disappear; they shrink and expand, but they are always with us, massive and deep. The variations in size of the Martian polar caps are much greater.

When sufficient magnification discloses Mars as a disk, the polar caps are the first features to be seen, contrasting strongly with the brickdust-red or deep-orange ball. Cassini, as early as 1666, described these areas as covered with a bright, whitish deposit that looked like snow, fixed in position and variable in size. From these observations it was concluded that they were at the poles of the planet and were composed of snow.

The true nature of the polar caps has been disclosed only recently. At the turn of the century planetary temperatures were beginning to be understood, and it was realized that the temperatures on Mars were very low. One segment of the astronomical fraternity discarded the snow theory, suggesting that the polar caps consisted of carbon dioxide in solid form—our "dry ice." It was Dr. Johnstone Stoney, who gave the electron its name, who proposed the carbon dioxide theory in 1903.

Only recently has evidence piled up which completely refutes the carbon-dioxide hypothesis of the polar caps. The most significant and conclusive work has been done by Kuiper, using the 82-inch McDonald Observatory telescope.

In 1948 he obtained the infrared spectrum of the north polar cap of Mars. It was similar to the spectrum obtained when sunlight is passed through a layer of water about a twenty-fifth of an inch thick. This led him to think in terms of frozen water in various forms, so he obtained the spectra of snow in various forms—melting, freshly fallen, and as hoarfrost deposited on plates super-cooled with dry ice. In every case the laboratory spectra from snow showed a marked resemblance to the spectrum of the Martian polar cap.

One phenomenon noted in photographs of Mars in various colors is that in the infrared the polar caps almost or entirely vanish. Kuiper proceeded to show that terrestrial snow and hoarfrost are black when viewed in the near infrared region, whereas carbon dioxide remains white much farther out in that region.

If this evidence is not enough, we can consider that on Mars dry ice can not continuously exist at a temperature above 230 degrees below zero, Fahrenheit, and this rules out this material, because the temperatures on Mars are far above this figure.

Today astronomers are convinced that the polar caps

are composed of water in some form, as there were many who believed it 50 years ago. The Lowell group clung tenaciously to the idea that the polar caps were water in one of its many states, but even they were not the first ones. Sir William Herschel, more than a century ago, assiduously observed Mars with his great telescopes and noticed variations in the polar caps intimately tied to the seasons on Mars. He concluded that the caps consisted of snow.

In the depth of winter the southern polar cap of Mars expands until it reaches latitude 50 degrees; when it is winter in the northern hemisphere, that cap reaches to latitude 60 degrees. The average shrinkage in summer is considerable; the northern cap becomes only about six degrees in diameter, while the minimum diameter of the southern cap, on the average, is about five degrees. There are instances when the southern cap has disappeared.

This variation of the southern cap from 80 degrees to five or less, as contrasted with the variation of the northern cap from 60 degrees to six, is due to the way the planet's orbit is oriented. Mars is farthest from the sun when the southern hemisphere has its winter, and nearest the sun when it is summer in that hemisphere. At its greatest extent the south polar cap of Mars has an area of over four million square miles.

Curiously the polar caps are not centered on the poles of rotation of Mars. The center of the southern cap is about seven degrees away from the areographic pole— about 250 miles from it. The difference for the northern cap is noticeable, but not quite so great.

The deterioration of the polar caps presents an interesting chain of phenomena. For a few months after the end of winter (March 21, Mars date), the polar cap grows smaller, at first barely noticeably, then at an accelerated rate. By the first week in May, Mars date, the boundary has become broken and irregular and dark rifts appear in the cap. These rifts grow steadily, splitting the cap into many sections; in some instances bright patches persist and are left behind to disappear at a later date. During July, Mars date, the decrease in size goes on, but at a reduced rate which ends in the cap of least size, a tiny white button on the planet.

The predictable regularity in the appearance of certain features in the receding polar cap both in time and in position on the planet indicates that peculiarities of the surface, perhaps differences in levels, influence the recession of the cap.

About the middle of September, Mars date, diffuse bright patches begin to appear in the polar region. These spread rapidly, finally obscuring the entire area down to the temperate zone. These must be bright and unstable atmospheric clouds or veils, and they persist through the fall and into the winter. Then the polar cap itself emerges, at first rather dull, and then becoming exceedingly large, very bright and white.

To behave in this fashion, the polar caps must be exceedingly thin. Many reasons can be advanced for this conclusion. To begin, the reflected light from a cap is significantly less than that from a thick layer of snow. The polar caps reflect about half of the light falling on them, whereas thick snow reflects about three quarters of the incident light. And computations taking into account the intensity of sunlight on Mars and the rate of shrinking of the polar caps indicate that they cannot exceed ten inches in depth nor can they be thinner than about 0.1 inch. A value of from one to two inches equivalent layer of compact ice is acceptable at this time.

It is not at all certain that the polar caps are composed wholly of snow. Russian astronomers at the 1939 opposition photographed the planet in various colors, and from their study of the results concluded that the surface brightness could be best explained by assuming the caps to be made of compact layers of ice. Others have suggested that these results could be equally well explained by assuming that there is both snow or hoarfrost and ice in the caps.

In 1951 Dollfus performed some significant experiments which further proved the water character of the polar caps. Knowing that the water came down in some form under conditions foreign to the earth, he set up a laboratory experiment to duplicate the conditions on Mars. He cooled a metal plate with liquid air, then put it into a vacuum chamber where the pressure was reduced to that of the Martian atmosphere. By introducing water vapor he induced the deposition of a fine granular frost on the metal plate and then measured the polarization of light reflected from the plate.

The significant result was that the surface exhibited polarization characteristics identical with those of the polar caps of Mars. For this it can be concluded that a light dust-like deposit similar to hoarfrost condenses on the frozen polar cap regions at a low temperature.

The evidence of the water content of the polar caps appears to be overwhelming, so this question seems to have been completely resolved for the astronomer. There is water on the planet, sometimes locked up in the caps, sometimes at least partially in liquid form due to melting. Now let's turn our attention to an obscure though important phenomenon concerned with the very edges of the polar caps.

When the bright cap retreats, a continuous dark fringe, which Lowell found to be of a dark blue-green color, is seen on its border. It is very hard to see, and some astronomers have claimed that it is an optical illusion due to contrast between the bright cap and the darker surface of the planet. It is not found on photographs, and some observers claimed that this fringe did not obey the laws of perspective as the planet rotated. Others considered it to be a real marking, for a variety of reasons, one of which was the change in the fringe itself with the passage of time.

As the polar cap shrinks in the Martian spring, the dark border or fringe, a band several hundred miles wide, suggests the existence of a region where the Martian soil has been dampened by the rapidly melting snows. When the melting of the cap is going on at the greatest rate, the dark fringe is most fully developed. As melting continues and the polar cap shrinks, the fringe also shrinks, apparently keeping pace with the cap; it becomes narrower, perhaps indicating a lessening of the water supply. By summer, when the polar cap is a mere button, the fringe has disappeared.

Problems arise as a result of these observations. For instance, it is well known that water vaporizes faster at reduced pressures, and with the low atmosphere pressure on Mars it is difficult to see why ice or snow would melt. It would seem that the snow would sublime, or vaporize, without the intermediate step of melting, just as in very cold weather a clean ice cube on the back window sill will disappear without melting.

There have been answers proposed to this question, mostly of the nature that both melting and sublimation can go on concurrently under the conditions on Mars. Liquid water can exist there, and it may be that the atmosphere directly over a polar cap is already so laden with water vapor that evaporation is retarded and melting can go on. Especially during the more rapid phases of shrinking of the cap there must be appreciable water to be released both to the atmosphere and to the adjacent soil.

Just how much water is there on Mars and in its atmosphere? At the Lowell Observatory in 1908 V. M. Slipher took photographs of the spectrum of Mars in the attempt to detect the bands due to water vapor. His results were unacceptable to most astronomers and other observers, particularly at Mount Wilson Observatory, using the 100-inch telescope, repeated the observations.

Dr. Theodore Dunham came to the conclusion that, area for area, the water vapor in the atmosphere of Mars could amount to no more than 0.15 per cent of that in the earth's atmosphere. Some scientists felt that Dunham went too far in this estimate because of a lack of precise knowledge of the amount of water vapor in the atmosphere above Mount Wilson. On the average there is in the atmosphere of the earth the equivalent of about a third of an inch of water. The measures at Mount Wilson led to a value of a maximum of less than 1/57 of an inch and a minimum of more than 1/2500 of an inch. Provisionally, de Vaucouleurs, one of the best modern students of Mars, would accept 1/250 of an inch as the water available on Mars.

S. L. Hess, a meteorologist, studying the clouds of Mars, believes that about one fortieth of an inch of water may be available, but this value turns out to be a good bit higher than the spectroscopic evidence will permit. From all of this it can be concluded that such measurements are intrinsically difficult, and the results merit little confidence. However, we can be sure that Mars is a rather arid planet.

We might proceed to a determination of the probable amount of water in the polar caps, when the southern cap is at its greatest extension. The area is about four million square miles, and we might assume an equivalent thickness of solid ice of about 0.4 inches. Then the total mass of water involved turns out to be about 100 thousand million tons. Spread this amount of water over the whole surface of Mars and the maximum amount of precipitable water turns out to be about 1/75 of an inch. As at any given time a good bit of this is locked up in the polar caps, the amount of water vapor in the atmosphere can be considered the 1/250 of an inch, which is de Vaucouleurs's value.

It is safe to conclude that on the entire surface of Mars there is less water than there is in one of our Great Lakes. And there must be a complete absence of lakes or pools of water on the surface. A pool only 300 yards in diameter would reflect the sun's light at certain angles and be spotted from earth, but no such flashes of light have ever been observed, so we can conclude that few, if any, exist.

The Canals

The director of the Milan Observatory was a highly competent observer. With his excellent 8½-inch telescope he scanned the heavens and paid particular attention to the surface of Mars. Since 1840 maps had been drawn and every map seemed to add detail to the preceding one. In 1877 Schiaparelli turned his telescope to Mars at a favorable opposition, planning to record the details of the surface on a new map. The seeing must have been ideal, for he saw strange, faint, dusky streaks at the critical limit of visibility, which means that sometimes they appeared to be there and sometimes not. But they remained visible long enough for him to record them, and the resulting drawing was the first in which man recorded the delicate straight-line markings on the planet. He named these markings *canali,* an Italian word meaning channels.

The surprising thing about this discovery is that no one took Schiaparelli seriously. Indeed, why should they? These streaks had been seen many times before by skilled, acute-visioned observers, but no one had bothered either to call particular attention to them or to map them. It remained for Schiaparelli to name them and to recognize them as stable features of the Martian surface. He saw these faint, evanescent streaks darting across the continents, apparently linking the seas. Continuous observation disclosed that all the continents were laced by networks of fine lines darker than the continents. Some canals extended for a few hundred miles, while others ran for thousands of miles in essentially regular lines. Some were seen consistently, and Schiaparelli assumed them to be more than 100 miles wide; others on the limit of visibility were thought to be from ten to 20 miles wide. They intersected at all possible angles, and at each point of intersection there was a small spot of pronouncedly darker color which Schiaparelli interpreted as a small lake.

In 1879 there was another favorable opposition, and again he drew the canals in precisely the same places. During his observations he was suddenly surprised to see one of the *canali* as double. He was convinced that these streaks were permanent markings, but nine years were to pass until in 1888 the French astronomers Perrotin and Thollon, using the 30-inch telescope at the Nice Observatory, saw the canals. Then in swift succession other observers in various parts of the world recognized these strange markings, some of them resolved into two parallel lines like a set of railroad tracks.

A few years later these markings were destined to become the most controversial topic in all of astronomy. The noted astronomer W. H. Pickering saw them at the Harvard Station in Arequipa, Peru, in 1892. Two years later Percival Lowell and A. E. Douglass at Flagstaff, Arizona, saw the canals not only on the continents but, like Pickering, on the seas! It was this observation that immediately convinced Lowell that there was no open water on Mars.

Lowell devoted a tremendous amount of effort, energy, and money to the mapping of the canals; year after year he completed maps which showed increased detail until finally, over the entire surface of both the bright and dark areas, there was an incredibly fine network of straight lines numbering at least 700. Like Schiaparelli, Lowell saw the canals extending for hundreds of miles, and in a few instances for three or four thousand miles. They continued their courses across the continents and seas with no deviation due to boundaries. Upon close examination many appeared to terminate at the bays or gulfs, as though there were something about them that required their presence at these points. To Lowell as to Schiaparelli three or more were seen to intersect at a small round or oval area which Lowell called, for obvious reasons, an "oasis"; many of these intersections are dotted over the maps published by Lowell. The majority of the oases were 120 to 150 miles in diameter, but many smaller ones were observed; like the canals, the oases flourished with the seasons.

That perfect seeing conditions are necessary can be judged from Lowell's account of the appearance of the canals. He indicates that when Mars is first observed, only the gross features like the polar caps and the seas are seen. However, if the observations are continued, the observer suddenly will ". . . be made aware of a vision as of a thread stretched somewhere from the blue-green across the orange areas of the disk." The thread immediately disappears, leaving the observer wondering what it was and trying to recall what he saw. Then, suddenly, once again there is the thread. Once more it disappears; this continues for some time, with the observer at all times wondering if what he has seen is real. That it is real is finally attested by the conformity of detail as recorded by many observers.

The observations made by Lowell led to an elaborate hypothesis in 1906. In his book *Mars and its Canals* he suggested that the network of canals and oases seemed to be a stupendous engineering project by living beings endowed with intelligence. These "Martians" had fashioned the canals to circulate and distribute the meager supply of water provided by the seasonal melting of the polar caps. Lowell thought the canals to be, instead of wide waterways like the Panama Canal or Suez Canal, the thin band of vegetation on each side of a narrow irrigation canal. Martians, reasoned Lowell, would be able to see similar markings on earth, in the Nile River Valley or that of the Mississippi. Ingeniously Lowell postulated that as soon as the snows melt the water is pumped into the canals and vegetation develops. If the water from a single canal does not suffice, a second is opened, thus accounting for the doubling of many of the canals.

Most astronomers did not agree with Lowell, and the controversy was on. In Europe skilled observers held that the canals were so situated on irregular natural surfaces that under certain conditions of seeing there appeared to be straight-line markings. The superb observer Antoniadi insisted that the surface of Mars was a Saharalike desert and he was supported by a majority of skilled observers with large telescopes at their disposal.

In the United States some observers saw them, others did not. Foremost among the American observers who disputed the existence of the thin line markings was E. E. Barnard, who had the reputation of being one of the keenest-eyed astronomers of all time. He observed Mars with the largest refractor in the world, the 40-inch at the Yerkes Observatory of the University of Chicago, and with the second-largest, the 36-inch at the Lick Observatory of the University of California. He noted that the surface was wonderfully full of detail but he could not see the thin, spidery lines as Schiaparelli had drawn them. Barnard fully believed that the canals seen by Schiaparelli were nonexistent and he was certain that future observations at favorable oppositions would prove this.

Photography was called into the argument, but when the image of Mars is magnified sufficiently to present a sizable disk, the surface brightness is so low that a fairly long exposure is necessary. Even with the great 200-inch telescope on Palomar Mountain an exposure of about one twentieth of a second is necessary, and in that interval there is usually at least one little wave of bad seeing to blur the image, however slightly. However, on a few of the many thousands of photographs made from the 7000-foot altitude of the Lowell Observatory there are indications of some of the more prominent canals. Photography can not soon settle this controversy.

The canals were undoubtedly observed before Schiaparelli's time. With his 8½-inch telescope he barely made them out. With larger telescopes the canals were more easily seen, but there still appears to be a limit to the size of the telescope that will show the canals. It is perhaps very significant that amateurs, many of them using moderate-sized homemade telescopes from their backyards, often see and draw the canals today, while many professional observers, using the greatest telescopes on earth, see something different.

In 1909 George E. Hale, the founder of the Yerkes, the Mount Wilson, and the Palomar Mountain observatories, observed Mars with the 60-inch reflector on Mount Wilson. On a night of exceptional seeing, using a low magnification, he found the straight-line markings as depicted on Lowell's drawings. With a magnification of 800 diameters, the regular markings broke down into heterogenous blobs and splotches. Similarly E. M. Antoniadi, using the 33-inch telescope at Meudon, saw the so-called canals as fortuitous alignments of irregular markings. In 1948 Kuiper, with the 82-inch reflector at McDonald Observatory under excellent observing conditions, said, "I have never seen a long, narrow canal nor a network of fuzzy canals! I am personally convinced that the objective evidence which has led to this concept has been misinterpreted and erroneously represented on the drawing."

There is no doubt that Percival Lowell drew the most elaborate network of canals. But few astronomers today recall that in 1894, when Lowell was beginning to build his reputation in this field, he described a similar network of canals on the planet Venus, a body which today we know to be perpetually cloud-enwrapped, so we can not see the surface of the planet! What could it be that leads some observers to see thin spidery sets of lines while other observers fail to see them?

Let's delve into the physio-psychological aspects of the problem. In discussing this with psychologists, the author finds that the eye is regarded as an almost perfect optical instrument. The trouble is that it is tied to the brain! As a result there is never a true picture, except on the retina of the eye; the brain superposes on this picture a little memory, past experience, prejudice, physical condition, until the final interpreted picture no longer resembles the true scene, or resembles it superficially at best.

Particularly there is an integrating tendency, as with a picture in a newspaper. Look at one carefully and you will find that it is made up of a lot of little dots. The eye-brain combination conspires to deliver up an impression of solid areas, or delicately shaded tones, from a mass of little dots of equal spacing but unequal size. Take a close look at a color illustration in a magazine and you'll find mixtures of little dots or circles of a few colors, which blend to give delicate shades that do not exist on the printed page. Similarly your color film and color TV achieve their colors of all shades by mixtures of only three different colors.

Now let's consider again the question of the visibility and the nature of the canals of Mars. The great mathematical astronomer Simon Newcomb was never noted as an observer, and perhaps the fact that he couldn't see the canals through the 40-inch telescope at Yerkes made him suspicious of observers of fine detail on Mars. He stretched wires and cords across various types of backgrounds, at various distances, and had other astronomers with excellent vision try to see them. He was able from this experiment to conclude that in order to be visible on Mars a canal would need to be seven miles wide. Next Newcomb measured the lengths of all the canals on the maps drawn by Percival Lowell. Adding them up and multiplying by seven miles, Newcomb then arrived at the total area of the canals, if they were all real. He arrived at a figure of about 33,000,000 square miles, which is about three fifths of the total area of Mars! This is obviously ridiculous, because only a glance at one of Lowell's maps of Mars serves to show that the canals don't cover even 1 per cent of the surface. Yet to be visible at all they would need to cover 60 per cent. Obviously, then, Newcomb concluded, many if not all of Lowell's canals could not exist.

At Flagstaff Lowell similarly stretched wires at various distances, and found a value different from Newcomb's. A wire somewhat less than a fifteenth of an inch in diameter was visible at a distance of about 1800 feet. Translating this to Mars as seen through a telescope, Lowell concluded that the narrowest canals could be as little as one mile wide, instead of seven miles as Newcomb had calculated, or ten miles as Schiaparelli had suggested. The widest canals, said Lowell, were about 30 miles in width. Nevertheless, even Lowell's one mile width leads to value of about 5,000,000 square miles for the total area of the canals, again greatly in conflict with Lowell's own representations of the planet.

Lowell recognized some of the defects of the eye when he stated that it was likely that if the canals were not extended lines, they would likely not be seen. Their sensible lengths guaranteed their visibility. A point is often too faint or too small to be seen, because it may stimulate only a single retinal rod or sensitive element; if instead of a point there is a fine line, many rods are excited and the line becomes visible. Their appearance is evidence that a canal-like property is inherent in some of the Martian markings. However, it can be easily demonstrated that a series of irregular blobs, arranged roughly in a line, will also be seen as a thin line resembling a Martian canal.

Simon Newcomb performed this experiment. He made a wash drawing on a circular disk, splotching a lot of haphazard chicken tracks on it. He set it up at a distance such that the apparent diameter of the disk matched that of Mars at a favorable opposition, seen through a good telescope. Then he had his observer friends at the Yerkes

Observatory view the disk and draw what they saw, both with the unaided eye and with a pair of opera glasses. The observers ended up with creditable sketches of a circular disk with nice, thin continuous canals over a large portion of it. It is perhaps interesting to note that the poorest drawing was made by W. H. Pickering, who always saw canals on Mars, while the best drawing of the artificial canals was made by E. E. Barnard, who could not see the Martian canals!

Newcomb added insult to injury in his next experiment. He blacked out all of a window in a darkened room except for an area as large as a sheet of paper. Observers inside the room, looking at the light shining through the paper, drew thin, straight "canals" on their sketches of a perfectly blank sheet of paper! A possible explanation is that there were little shreds and other bits of texture in the paper, but the fact remains that the integrating propensity of the eye-brain combination led to straight, regular lines.

In 1903 the English astronomer E. W. Maunder repeated Newcomb's wash-drawing experiment, with some 13-year-old boys at the Royal Hospital School as his observers. Again those students at the limit of distinct vision drew thin, straight lines like the canals of Mars, instead of the heterogeneous markings of the original drawing.

In all fairness it must be mentioned that the French astronomer Camille Flammarion repeated this experiment with French schoolboys, this time using dots instead of irregular blobs, and the boys did not draw these as illusory canals. It would be interesting to know the full details of this experiment, such as distance, size of dots, and that sort of thing. It is regrettable that Flammarion, who supported the many-canal school of observers, came out with the answer he wanted, whereas the same must be said to be true of Newcomb and Maunder, who were if anything somewhat opposed to the reality of the complicated network of Martian canals.

Perhaps the best criteria we have today are the statements formerly quoted from George E. Hale, E. M. Antoniadi, and Gerard Kuiper. Under ideal conditions, with good telescopes, the canals are not to be seen by competent observers. We may add another experience, that of A. Dollfus, observing with the 24-inch refractor of the Pic du Midi Observatory high in the French Pyrenees, a station where the seeing conditions are considered to be about the finest in the world. In February, 1948, Dollfus found that on nights when he considered the seeing to be ordinary, the canals in the region of Syrtis Major could be seen plainly and clearly, and he made some magnificent sketches of surface detail, rivaling or surpassing the most elaborate turned out by Lowell. However, using the same equipment on nights of *superb* seeing, he no longer saw the straight-line thin canals, but instead broken lines of markings which formerly he had integrated into a geometrical pattern.

Here again is definite substantiation of what Newcomb in 1897 and Maunder in 1903 were trying to show. Markings at the very limit of visibility are more or less unconsciously patterned into nonexistent lines and geometrical figures. If the observer wishes hard enough to see artificial markings, he can see them; if he goes beyond what he wishes, he is likely not to see them, under the finest conditions.

White clouds were the first to be seen and recognized as such. Then there are the yellow ones first recognized in 1879. And then there are the blue clouds, possibly a distinct species, possibly a variant of the white ones.

Most of us are familiar with the fact that infrared radiation penetrates haze and cloud, while light of shorter wave length has a hard time getting through. Most photographs of the ground taken from airplanes are made with deep red or infrared, for this reason. And astronomers have long used this technique to investigate the atmospheres of Mars and other planets. When various filters are used for such photographs of Mars, the atmospheric phenomena of the planet show up strongly in violet and ultraviolet, while the surface is shown best in infrared.

As early as 1926 Dr. W. H. Wright, at the Lick Observatory on Mt. Hamilton, California, classified the clouds into two groups—those that showed up most strongly in ultraviolet and those that could be seen in infrared. The former were presumed to be in the atmosphere, the latter close to the surface. He did not mention the blue clouds specifically, so they must have been included with the white ones, high in the atmosphere.

Visual observations of Mars tell us a little about the blue clouds. They have been likened to the icy haze which comes with frost on earth. From the amount and kind of polarization of the light from them Dollfus at Pic du Midi has concluded that they are like the high-level, ice-crystal, mother-of-pearl clouds seen over the earth's polar regions. To anticipate somewhat, we may say that at an altitude of about 12 miles the temperature and pressure of the earth's atmosphere and that of Mars are quite similar. The blue clouds, found at altitudes from six to 19 miles above the surface of Mars, may well be composed of tiny ice crystals. But not all astronomers are sure that there is a real distinction to be drawn between the blue clouds and the white ones, and perhaps they will once more be classed together.

While white clouds are seen in the central regions of the disk at times, many of them appear at the edge of the planet where the sun is just rising. They seem not to rotate with the planet, and are therefore considered to be condensations of some material, probably ice crystals of considerable size, forming during the night and melting quickly, within an hour, under the influence of the sun's radiation.

Another type of phenomenon classed with the clouds in the Martian atmosphere is the violent layer or blue haze. It probably consists of tiny nonspherical particles suspended high above the surface. At times, for periods of perhaps a few days, this layer seems to clear away, permitting unexcelled observation of the surface details of the planet. There have been various suggestions concerning the nature of the particles composing this layer: meteoric dust, ice or carbon-dioxide crystals, or a combination of various materials. Perhaps the layer is a double one, the lower layer of water ice crystals (like mare's-tails in our atmosphere), the higher one of carbon-dioxide crystals. This is an extraordinary mysterious and interesting phenomenon—this blue haze.

In 1954 a group of observers went to work to keep Mars under 24-hour surveillance from observatories scattered in longitude across the earth. For the first time, in 1953, an

International Mars Committee had been formed; consisting of astronomers, physicists, and meteorologists, this committee planned the observational program on an international scale, and from its work there emerged many valuable hints that will be of value in future planetary observations.

Because of the almost continuous scrutiny of Mars in 1954 many intriguing details formerly noted only in scattered fashion could be continuously pursued. For example, the blue haze seemed to clear up on the afternoon side of the planet, become quite transparent at sunset, then reform at sunrise. For the past 30 or more years similar phenomena had occasionally been observed, especially at oppositions of the planet, but in 1954 the blue haze became almost completely transparent from May until July 2; during this period good photographs of the surface were made even in blue light. And it was during this period that E. C. Slipher, observing with the 27-inch refractor of the Lamont-Hussey Observatory at Bloemfontein, South Africa, discovered definite cloud belts on the planet.

Also at this time an odd W-shaped cloud was discovered on the sunset limb of Mars, by Mount Wilson observers. Comparison with photographs taken elsewhere revealed the interesting fact that this cloud formed every afternoon, then disappeared before sunrise came to that area of Mars. There were four bright knobs in this cloud, three at the sharp angles of the W and one at one end. They correspond roughly in position with the oases Arsea Silva, Ascraeus Lacus, Tithonius Lacus, and Hebes Lacus; two of the strokes of the W corresponded to the canals Ulysses and Fortunae. As yet the interpretation of the cloud and its correspondence with the surface features has not been forthcoming, but doubtless this feature will be one of the most carefully observed during succeeding oppositions.

Here we have seen definite direct observational evidence of the existence of an atmosphere on Mars. And, in a way, we can liken the behavior of Martian clouds to that of clouds in our own atmosphere. Morning haze is not uncommon on earth, followed by clearing in the afternoon, then formation of clouds at sunset. And occasionally on earth, in desert areas, there are sandstorms. On Mars the yellow clouds are among the most conspicuous but have a wide range of brightness. Almost all observers have agreed that they are composed of dust particles and that they ride rather low in the atmosphere. Antoniadi, in the twenties, suggested that their behavior is exactly what we should expect. They are most numerous when Mars is closest to the sun, because the increased solar radiation produces more convection and stronger winds to raise the dust from the surface.

One objection to this theory was advanced because the clouds are not of the same color as the general surface, but it is reasonable to suppose that only the smallest particles of dust can be raised into the thin atmosphere. The more highly pulverized a material the lighter, in general, is its color. There seems little reason to doubt that the yellow clouds are dust storms that raise tiny particles that occasionally obscure the surface markings of Mars and even cast a lighter color over the whole face of the planet.

One astronomer, Dr. Dean B. McLaughlin at the University of Michigan, has developed an hypothesis that many if not most of the major markings on Mars are pro-

duced by the deposition of fresh dust from Martian volcanoes. The general tendency of the markings, in his
opinion, is exactly what should prevail as a result of strong
trade winds on the planet. The supposed seasonal changes,
then, would be the result of the seasonal variation in intensity of the winds; instead of vegetation, the greenish
markings would be freshly deposited volcanic debris. A
newly developed area such as the Thoth-Nepenthes would
be evidence that a new volcano had broken out. So far
there has been little agreement of other astronomers with
this idea, but the fact remains that there have been a few
scattered observations of bright spots of light and other
phenomena which may sometime be interpreted as volcanic outbreaks on Mars.

Bernard Lyot at Pic du Midi studied the polarization of
light from Mars and found that in general it resembled
that of the light from the moon; dust storms of Mars reduced the degree of polarization. We believe the moon's
surface to be covered with at least a thin layer of dust, so
Kuiper and others have concluded that possibly the bright
regions of Mars are also dust-covered.

Mars has a diameter only a little more than half that of
the earth, and its mass is much less, so the gravitational
field at the surface of the planet must be less than that of
the earth. Essentially there are two factors that work together to control the ability of a planet to retain an atmosphere. One of these is the surface gravity, the other the
distance of the planet from the sun. The first tells us how
strongly the particles of an atmosphere are held to the
planet, the second tells us how fast the particles will move
about in the atmosphere. Actually the surface gravity

should be expressed in terms of what is called the velocity of escape—which for the earth, for example, is seven miles per second. This means that a particle traveling away from the earth's surface with a speed of seven miles per second can overcome the earth's gravitational attraction and escape into outer space.

Many years ago the brilliant English astronomer Sir James Jeans showed that when the mean velocity of the particles of a gas in the atmosphere of a planet is less than a fifth of the escape velocity, the atmosphere will be stable for periods of the order of thousands of millions of years. On Mars the velocity of escape is 3.1 miles per second, and only the very lightest gases, hydrogen and helium, at the temperatures existing on Mars, will have mean velocities higher than about 0.6 miles per second. These gases, then, would be lost to Mars, while carbon dioxide, argon, molecular oxygen and nitrogen, water vapor and even atomic nitrogen and oxygen could be retained by the gravitational field of Mars.

Kuiper, from the relative scattering powers of the atmospheres of the earth and Mars, has concluded that the Martian atmosphere consists of 96 per cent nitrogen, about four per cent argon and 0.3 per cent carbon dioxide. This is to be compared with 78 per cent nitrogen, 21 per cent oxygen, 0.9 per cent argon, and 0.03 per cent carbon dioxide in the atmosphere of the earth. We know that water is present on Mars in various states—probably liquid water is exceedingly scarce—and we know, too, that water can be broken up into hydrogen and oxygen by action of sunlight, to at least a slight degree, but these two gases at best would exist in such minute amounts on Mars that we can

ignore them. The presence of argon need not seem surprising because on Mars as on earth it would result from
the radioactive decay of potassium. Indeed, this gas is even
believed to be present in slight amounts on the moon, although we have no direct evidence of it.

This, then, is the postulated composition of the atmosphere of Mars. What do we definitely know, and how is
this information obtained?

The astronomer works under a very severe handicap
when we compare his situation with, say, the physicist or
chemist. While other scientists can use all of their senses—
touch, smell, taste, hearing, sight—the astronomer is restricted to the single sense of sight. Everything the astronomer knows about extraterrestrial objects must come to
him as a result of his interpretation of the radiations that
reach him from those objects. Despite this incredible handicap, the astronomer has been able to gather a wealth of
information concerning distant celestial objects. Someday
he may land on the moon and Mars and other bodies relatively nearby, and then put his other senses into play, but
just now he must depend upon what he can learn from
waves of energy that come from these bodies.

The most important tool in the astronomer's kit has
been the spectroscope. Light from the source that is to be
analyzed passes through a thin slit, then through a lens,
before passing through a prism; then a viewing telescope
or a camera is used to deliver the final image of what is
called the spectrum of the source. In astronomy the spectroscope is attached to the eye-end of a telescope, and the
telescope itself then becomes merely a collector of light
for the spectroscope.

Suppose, now, we use a spectroscope to analyze the light of the sun. We see the continuous spectrum—the rainbow band of color—produced by the inner portion of the sun's bulk, where the pressures are greater. But crossing this band are dark absorption lines, produced as the light from inside the sun passes through the thinner gases near its surface, and each atom subtracts some of the energy from the light. Now atoms of hydrogen subtract only certain bits of energy—produce only certain absorption lines—and no other. Similarly atoms of other materials absorb only their characteristic energies, and produce unique patterns of lines. By measuring the positions of the absorption lines in any spectrum we can determine the composition of the gas through which the light has passed on its way to us.

We must always take into account the earth's atmosphere, because light from celestial bodies must pass through it before arriving at our spectroscopes, but we can do that in various ways. And when we analyze the atmosphere of a planet, such as Mars, we must realize that the planet has no light of its own. What we receive is sunlight, reflected from the planet, and in a way "polluted" by having passed down through the planet's atmosphere, and then back out again to get to us. But we know the spectrum of sunlight and can make allowances for it.

Until recently the astronomer was unsuccessful in determining any constituents of the Martian atmosphere. But in 1947 Dr. Kuiper, with the spectroscope attached to the 82-inch McDonald telescope in Texas, succeeded in detecting the bands due to carbon dioxide, in the infrared region of the spectrum of Mars; the amount of this gas in the atmosphere of Mars was computed to be about twice the percentage of that in the earth's atmosphere.

As a vital life element oxygen was the first gas to be searched for in the Martian atmosphere. Early in this century Percival Lowell proposed a means of determining spectroscopically the amount of oxygen, but the inferior equipment and grosser methods of analysis led to ambiguous results, yet indicating the presence of oxygen. At the 1932-33 opposition of the planet the 100-inch telescope at Mount Wilson, then the largest in the world, was used to obtain ten good spectrograms of the planet. From measures of 30 oxygen lines on each plate the conclusion was drawn that the lines were due to oxygen in the earth's atmosphere and that there could be no more oxygen in the atmosphere of Mars than about 1/1000 as much as we have here. This was on the basis of mile per mile of surface area, so the total amount of oxygen in the atmosphere of Mars would be below that figure, inasmuch as the planet is smaller than earth. A subsequent recomputation has raised this figure slightly; it may be that Mars possesses, over each square mile, 0.15 per cent as much oxygen as exists over the average square mile of the earth's surface—truly an insignificant amount.

This question now poses itself: Why, if there is so much oxygen in our atmosphere, is there so little, if any, in the Martian atmosphere? The two planets are not widely dissimilar, and any hypothesis for the formation of the solar system supposes the planets to be coeval. The velocity of escape from Mars is lower than that for earth, but there is one even more important factor we haven't yet taken care of. The temperature at Mars must be considered to be not simply that due to solar radiation at the surface but that in the high atmosphere, where oxygen would act to raise the temperature and thus to accelerate its own escape from the planet. For example, an atmosphereless earth at our present distance of the sun would have a mean temperature of about freezing—32 degrees F.—yet in our atmosphere at heights of hundreds of miles the effective or kinetic temperature is many thousands of degrees.

Except for the effects of the lower value of gravity and the somewhat greater distance from the sun, the evolution of the atmosphere of Mars could be expected to be quite similar to that of our atmosphere. In the pre-protoplanet days of our earth there were ammonia, methane, and water here, and there must have been the same gases on Mars. Nitrogen, carbon dioxide, and oxygen evolve from these primordial atmospheric materials. On Mars we have found carbon dioxide; nitrogen can be inferred, and we have seen that there may be a faint trace of oxygen. Many students of this problem believe that the oxygen in our atmosphere is largely due to the presence of living things here; from this we could argue that Mars never has sheltered the kinds and quantities of life that have existed on earth.

Again the presence of argon in the atmosphere of Mars is only inferred, on the assumption that radioactive potassium probably exists there, as it does on earth. Similarly the other heavy inert gases—neon, krypton, xenon, and radon—can readily exist there, in minute amounts. Unfortunately these gases do not all produce absorption lines of any considerable intensity in easily observed regions of the spectrum, and their amounts would be quite slight, so we have no direct evidence of them. It will be possible to verify our deductions concerning the atmosphere of Mars only when scientists actually set foot on the planet or at least approach near enough to permit a bottle full of the atmosphere to be obtained for analysis.

Because of the lower surface gravity the pressures in the Martian atmosphere must be much less than those in our atmosphere. As far back as 1822 Sir John Herschel observed an occultation of a star by Mars. As the planet moved along to hide the star, there was a sharp disappearance, and not a fading, and Herschel concluded that the atmosphere of Mars must be very tenuous.

Estimates of the surface pressure of the atmosphere on Mars have been made, of the order of two to six inches of mercury, as compared with the average 30 inches of mercury at sea level for the earth; this would correspond to a weight of one to three pounds per square inch, as compared with earth's almost 15 pounds.

Dr. Donald H. Menzel in 1925 proposed a method that first involved calculating the total mass of the atmosphere, which might be determined by the way light is scattered in the atmosphere. Measuring the reflecting power or albedo of Mars in both visual and photographic light would permit this factor to be determined. The result was a value of slightly more than one pound per square inch for the weight of the atmosphere of the planet.

Lyot and Dollfus, at Pic du Midi, used polarization methods and obtained a surface pressure of slightly more than two pounds per square inch.

Various other methods, including even an application of theoretical meteorology, as well as measurements of brightnesses in visual and photographic light, have been applied, with rather consistent results. The weighted mean of the acceptable values indicates that the surface pressure of the atmosphere of Mars is about one and a quarter pounds per square inch—the value in the earth's atmosphere at an altitude of 11 or 12 miles, twice as high as Mount Everest.

But there is an interesting additional phenomenon that we should pursue. Because of the lower gravitational attraction at the surface of Mars the pressures and densities of the atmosphere are lower than ours only in the lower levels. The lower gravitational pull also tells us that there is a lower gradient in the atmosphere of Mars; the atmosphere thins out more slowly than ours does. Our atmosphere and that of Mars have the same density at about 20 miles above the respective surfaces, at a point where the pressure has fallen to about one quarter pound per square inch. Above this height the pressure in the Martian atmosphere is actually *greater* than the pressure in our own atmosphere at equal heights.

One consequence of the lower atmospheric pressure at low altitudes on Mars will be extremely short twilight at both sunset and dawn. On earth twilight may last as long as one and a half hours. On an atmosphereless planet, like the moon, darkness comes as soon as the sunlight no longer falls on the surface. But the particles of an atmosphere scatter the sunlight and produce a less than black sky that continues to illuminate the surface. During the day on Mars the sky will appear much less bright than ours, and consequently the softening effect of skylight will be largely lacking; contrasts of light and shadow will seem extreme.

And the twilight on Mars will be extremely short. Measures of the twilight zone on Mars have been used to determine the effective thickness of the atmosphere of Mars.

This problem has been attacked since early observers noted that ultraviolet images of Mars, showing the atmosphere most strongly, appeared to be about 3 per cent larger than the infrared images which presumably showed only the ball of the planet itself. Later results indicated that the difference was actually greater, about 6 per cent. From these values an estimate of about 60 miles for the thickness of the atmospheric shell has been made.

But there are some who believe that this purely photographic determination is an effect of the photographic process or other factors and is not a proper way to determine the thickness of the atmosphere. For example, the Russian astronomer W. W. Scharonow believes that the red images fall off at the edges because of less light falling on the surface there, while the violet images are actually brighter at the edges, due to greater scattering. The differences between the two kinds of images then would be exaggerated.

In 1948 Kuiper observed Mars visually with various color filters and made careful measurements indicating that there is no difference in the diameter of Mars as viewed with violet and red light. The greatest difference there could be, he claims, would be only about 0.3 per cent, caused by the haze layer at a height of four to six miles, and this would be barely on the threshold of observation. Diametrically opposed to this finding is that of Dollfus, who in 1952 used a new micrometer to measure the differences in diameters as revealed by violet and red light observed visually, and found that some violet clouds were at an altitude of 75 miles above the surface of Mars. From these results it would appear that there is plenty of evidence for the existence of an atmosphere, but considerable uncertainty as to its extent.

The presence of an atmosphere on Mars will make the problem of landing a space ship on the planet's surface easier than landing on a completely atmosphereless object like the moon. Just as much power must be used in landing on the moon as is required to escape from it, and in space travel one of the most expensive commodities is fuel. It must be brought all the way from earth, to the space station first, thence to the moon.

The ferry rockets which will land on the surface of Mars will be streamlined vessels, much like our giant transport planes except that they will be rocket-driven instead of propeller-driven, and they will possess enormous wing areas to make use of the thinner atmosphere. These ferry rockets will sweep into the Martian atmosphere to take advantage of its braking power to slow them to nominal landing speeds. As we have seen earlier, the surface of Mars is so flat that extensive natural runways will be available for landing the space ships.

Another factor that will aid in setting down on the planet is the lower value of the surface gravity; a rocket ship will weigh only 0.38 as much as its weight on earth. The wing loading thus will be less, and sufficiently large wings can be designed to take advantage of the lift provided by even the thin Martian atmosphere.

Once a space ship has landed, conditions on Mars will not be too different from conditions aboard the ship.

There will still remain the necessity for a space suit to maintain the proper atmospheric pressure for survival. Oxygen regenerating plants will be necessary to furnish a continuous supply of this life-supporting gas. It is difficult to conceive of anything on the surface of the planet that could serve as food despite the fact that in some parts of the earth even lichens are used as a sort of food for human consumption. Perhaps the scant life we can hope to find on Mars might serve as fodder for lower animals that might be brought along as food for the humans.

If we were at the equator of Mars, the temperature at noon might rise as high as 80 degrees, but it would fall off during the afternoon much more rapidly than on earth, and at night would be about 80 degrees below zero. Night would come with startling suddenness, after a brief twilight following a late afternoon in which the darker sky would send but little light into the stark shadows. But the sky as seen from Mars might be well worth the trip. The thin atmosphere would not scatter light as ours does, and the sky would be the deepest midnight blue imaginable, practically black. We would see more stars with the unaided eye than we ever do at home, and they would shine with a steady light, not twinkling as on earth except during one of the rare storms. The Milky Way would present a magnificent spectacle of piled-up masses of bright and dark areas.

Not all nights on Mars would be crystal clear. Some nights would produce clouds as on earth, but they would not be the nimbus clouds that bring rain, or the fluffy, dense cumulus clouds. Instead, they would be like our high cirrus clouds, consisting of frozen water vapor. Except for dust storms that would require our protecting our instruments from the penetration of ultrafine abrasive sand, Mars would be a veritable astronomer's paradise.

The constellations would be quite familiar, the stars all standing in their proper places and of their familiar relative brightnesses. While it is true that we have changed our position in space, the nearest star is still 100,000 times as far away as the maximum distance between Mars and earth.

We would see meteors or shooting stars flashing against the deep background of the sky. If you are one who makes a wish on a meteor, on Mars you would be overwhelmed with opportunities, because on that planet you are nearer the region where travel the asteroids, or minor planets, and there is reason to believe that meteors will be 100 times as plentiful in the Martian sky as compared to ours. Many of them might be larger than the typical microscopic meteor that flashes in earth's atmosphere. And because the atmosphere of Mars is denser at very high altitudes than is the earth's, the meteor would begin to glow earlier and would glow probably more brightly.

The earth would be visible setting before midnight or rising after it, and it would be a brilliant bluish star. It would not be so bright as Venus appears to us on earth, but it would still be brighter than anything except the sun. Our moon would not likely be visible, because of its proximity to the earth in the sky.

If by any chance there should be an explosion of an atomic or a hydrogen bomb on the earth, it would be seen as an exceedingly brilliant flash. Through a telescope the land and sea areas could be easily differentiated, and the polar caps would wax and wane somewhat, and the continents would change color with the seasons. Storms would easily be visible, and perhaps great dust storms would obscure large areas. The giant rivers would be seen making their way to the seas, and even some of the large built-up areas could be seen, but hardly understood if we did not know from terrestrial experience that they were.

But Mars would be a lonesome place. Only our own companions would be available for talk and assistance. Conditions on the surface of the planet are so rigorous that we can be fairly certain that terrestrial-type animals could not exist there. But that there is life of some kind there we are equally certain, at least until we find some new observational evidence to refute our present opinions.

6

Life on Mars

In our discussion of the dark areas of Mars, and particularly in the story of the seasonal changes in these markings and the canals, we have anticipated somewhat the material of this chapter. But while it was hinted that these markings could result from a form of vegetable life, the point was not elaborated at that time because of the importance of the subject. There are a great many details to be treated, and many refinements of our thinking to be undertaken, before we can give our best definite answer to the question: Is there life on Mars?

Are there any tests which could resolve the problem of the existence of vegetation on the planet? The plants on our own planet have been thoroughly studied for many generations, and we understand them pretty well, but there still remain some mysteries in the details of the photosynthesis process—the mechanism of plant metabolism which permits a plant, in the presence of sunlight, to extract from its environment the materials necessary to nourish its body.

Our green plants contain chlorophyll, the coloring matter whose formation is only now being understood through the use of biological tracer elements such as radioactive carbon and phosphorus. This important plant material has a high reflectivity in the infrared and an absorption in the red. Therefore if Mars is photographed in infrared, or its spectrum in the red is obtained, we should be able to determine whether chlorophyll is present. This compound is not found. The dark areas certainly do not photograph as though they were green plants with chlorophyll content. Moreover the lack of oxygen in the atmosphere of Mars is an indication that this material is absent, because chlorophyll is the agent which frees oxygen. If approximately one third of the area of Mars is covered with greenish markings, the amount of oxygen in the atmosphere of Mars should be considerable, if chlorophyll is present. But we have seen earlier that the amount of oxygen over each square mile of Mars is of the order of less than one tenth of 1 per cent as much as exists over each square mile of the earth.

Kuiper has done considerable work on the correlation of the dark areas with terrestrial vegetation. He indicates that while it is true that the spectrum of chlorophyll does not show up in the light from the green areas, neither does it occur in certain types of terrestrial lichens and mosses, plants which appear to be well adapted to life under extreme conditions. In the lowest orders of plants the reflection curves led Kuiper to state that chlorophyll is present only in small quantities. And the absence of any trace of water in this reflection spectrum is explained by either the real absence of this material or its masking by an opaque and dry skin.

On earth climbers of the highest mountain peaks find that the last signs of life as they ascend higher and higher are the lichens that are seen to flourish even when clinging to bare rocks. These hardy plants are well adapted to low temperature and lack of water—more or less the kind of alpine or subarctic climate that exists on Mars. They are so hardy that the French physicist Paul Becquerel was able to revive lichens such as Xanthoria, after they had been dried in a vacuum for six years and then immersed in liquid air at a temperature of 300 degrees F. below zero! Even in liquid helium, at a temperature of more than 450 degrees F. below zero, and in a dry vacuum simultaneously, dehydrated spores of fungi and mosses remained viable and were later permitted to revive and give rise to normal plants. There are instances in which these plants have been stored for a century without dying.

Everywhere on earth some form of this kind of plant life can be found, be that place the Sahara Desert, where the temperature is always above 100 degrees F. during the day, the polar regions, where the temperature never gets above freezing, the dark cavern below the surface, or the regions which for months are in constant sunshine. They may very well live in that "shadowland" between the living and nonliving.

These primitive plants have developed a remarkable ability to adapt to rigorous conditions. Where the sunlight is intense and of long duration, they may develop dyes to act as filters to shield them from the ultraviolet which gets through the atmosphere. This answers one objection that has been raised against the existence of life on Mars. On earth we are protected from the ultraviolet of the sun by the absorption of most of this lethal radiation in a layer of ozone that lies in a layer about 20 miles above the surface. Now, ozone is produced from oxygen, and if there is no oxygen in the atmosphere of Mars, there is no ozone. But, on the other hand, life on earth has adapted to a condition of weak ultraviolet radiation from the sun, whereas lichens have demonstrated that they can protect themselves if there is too prolonged exposure to that which does leak through. On Mars we can expect this kind of adaptation to have gone considerably further.

When the temperature is low—say, 15 degrees F.—these primitive plants cease to respire—that is, to take in carbon dioxide and release some oxygen. They keep the oxygen within themselves, between their cells. And when the temperature gets to about 30 degrees F. below zero, the available water is used up, and the plant thus protects itself against freezing. Thus they seem to be capable of adapting to an extreme range of temperatures. In short, no matter how severe the conditions this most primitive form of plant life appears able to adapt and flourish.

Lichens are composed of two separate organisms: a fungus and some algae, living in symbiosis with the fungus as the senior member of the partnership. It is the fungus which provides protection from the cold. And, being hygroscopic, the fungus provides inorganic substances, including water, for the combination. The algae build up organic substances from the inorganic, by the process of photosynthesis. This process operates to build up carbohydrates in the plant by combining water and carbon dioxide; normally this occurs only in the presence of sunlight. As the carbohydrates are formed, oxygen is released to the atmosphere.

These plants are able to produce organic acids which decompose rock, and Dr. Hubertus Strughold points out that they may very well have been first kind of vegetation developing on bare volcanic rocks on earth; by breaking up these rocks and adding their own decayed substances they may have prepared the humus necessary for higher orders of plant life.

The algae need carbon dioxide, and it thus appears that this gas is the only absolute atmospheric requirement for the existence of vegetation.

The speed with which the green areas darken in the Martian spring is indicative of an intense metabolism—an exceptionally fast rate of living and growth. These plants must therefore consume large volumes of oxygen in respiration—oxygen obtained from the carbon dioxide of the atmosphere, separated by photosynthesis during the day, and stored in the form of an internal atmosphere exceedingly rich in oxygen. Thus, during the day the major part of the oxygen is immediately consumed by the plant, but a residual amount is available for respiration between twilight and dawn, when it is so cold that the plant practically becomes latent and needs very little oxygen. The ice crystals formed at low temperatures are outside the cells so that the organism is not injured by the freezing of the internal water.

Here, then, we may have the clue as to why oxygen is so scarce on a planet which may have as much as a third of its surface covered with plant life. Oxygen is formed,

but is assimilated by the plants themselves, and any minute amount that finds its way into the atmosphere may
be absorbed by oxygen-hungry materials on Mars, such as
metals and minerals.

In the minds of most astronomers there is little doubt
at this time that the green areas of Mars contain a form
of vegetation similar to our lichens. Certainly these primitive plants are hardy enough, and there appears to be no
compelling reason why they could not exist. However,
there are a few points in this reasoning that need to be
cleared up. On Mars there are distinct color changes correlated with the seasons. Lichens normally do not show
seasonal changes. How can we explain this anomaly?

The obvious answer is that the lichens on Mars are not
precisely identical with those on earth. It would be too
much to expect that the plant life on earth and that on
Mars should have followed exactly parallel courses of development down through eons of time, in view of the different conditions on the two planets. We do know that
under conditions of high altitude, low humidity, and low
temperature on earth there still exist species of lichens
which can thrive. Also, Bastin has pointed out that there
are some lichens that change color when subjected to
different humidities. The species P. *pulverulenta* seen frequently on tree trunks is deep green when moist and gray-
ish-green when dry. P. *caperata* is yellow-gray above, rough
and blackish beneath. Bastin writes, ". . . the handsomest
and most conspicuous of these leaf-like species is the
orange lichen which occurs very extensively on roofs, walls,
rocks and sometimes on ancient and stunted hawthorns.
On flat surfaces it slowly covers more or less circular areas,

and its bright yellow coloring is very attractive. The drier the situation the richer seems to be the tint, for examples found growing in moist and shady spots are usually pale yellow, or yellowish-green."

Either a flow of water from the poles or an increase in the humidity of the atmosphere with the melting of the polar caps would be sufficient to cause a color change, if the Martian lichens exhibit the same properties as some of the 15,000 varieties of terrestrial lichens.

There is another difficulty with the hypothesis that plant life exists on Mars. On earth the cooler regions are in the forests where plant metabolism is actively going on. That is the reason the woods are such delightful places in the summer. But our observations indicate that the "seas" of Mars are about 16 degrees F. warmer than the bright adjacent areas! Coblentz has found a rather high superficial temperature in the dark areas. However, he has found also that in the far north near the polar circle the temperature of illuminated surfaces covered with certain mosses and lichens can exceed that of the frozen ground by from 35 to 55 degrees F.! He gives the reason for this: ". . . the upper layer of a moss has a high absorption for solar radiation . . . while the thermal conductivity is low." Therefore the temperature of the upper surface increases to a higher level than if the material were sand or solid rock, and, moreover, this heat is lost more slowly. Here we may have a fine example of adaptation: Where the sun's radiation is weaker, the plant has adapted itself to greater utilization of it.

A theory by the Swedish physical chemist S. Arrhenius more than forty years ago proposed that the dark areas of

Mars were covered with hygroscopic substances that were subject to alternate periods of humidification and dessication and to the effect of ultraviolet radiation. This is in keeping with the idea, held by many at that time, that Mars is an ancient world that has lost all its waters; the salts in the old sea beds would pick up what little moisture there is in the atmosphere at certain seasons and would undergo the color changes seen. And a highly artificial choice of materials in the old salt beds could account for these changes.

However, the maximum humidity of the atmosphere of Mars is so very low that it is unlikely that this phenomenon could occur there, and the idea becomes even less tenable when we consider the general permanence of the dark markings. We know there are many dust storms, and the yellow deposits from these storms would in time cover up the darker material of the "seas." Only something that can renew itself each spring—thrusting its head, so to speak, above the newly deposited layer of dust—can be held accountable for the permanence of the markings.

By the same token the volcanic theory of the markings is not likely to be held valid. The reappearance of the canals and larger markings in the same places each year indicates that that wind-blown volcanic dust cannot account for them. Vegetation, defying the sand drifts and feeding on the yellow dust, appears to be the only explanation for the dark markings on Mars.

Now that we have concluded that vegetation is present on the surface of Mars, we come to the sequel: Could animal life exist there? In this let's follow the reasoning of A. E. Slater, who points out that in the formula for photosynthesis, six molecules of carbon dioxide and six molecules of water combine, in the presence of sunlight, into one molecule of carbohydrate and six molecules of oxygen. This presupposes, of course, that chlorophyll or some other substance is present, to make the transformation possible.

Now suppose we turn this equation end for end and write it as follows:

$$C_6H_{12}O_6 + 6O_2 \longrightarrow 6CO_2 + 6H_2O + \text{energy}$$

This formula is now the one for respiration—the "burning" of a carbohydrate molecule to release energy—a molecule of carbohydrate combines with six molecules of oxygen to form six molecules of carbon dioxide and six molecules of water. From this we see that precisely the same amount of oxygen is released as was absorbed initially.

Slater then writes:

> However, this process cannot go on indefinitely, unless the Martian plants are immortal. On the earth, when plants die, they usually become oxidized, either in the bodies of animals, or by decaying where they fall, and it will be seen from the formulae that the surplus oxygen they have put into the air while growing will be exactly used up when the same amount of tissue decays by oxidation.*

But not always. On the earth, during past geological ages, a vast amount of vegetation has been buried under water in swamps, etc., before it had time to be oxidized by decay, and has turned into coal; and other organisms

---

* Some might bring up the question of bacteroidal decay. While the author is cognizant of this possibility, he cannot see how this would alter the case he presents.

have similarly been buried unoxidized and turned into oil. The surplus oxygen, which might have been used to oxidize them but was not, must have remained in the atmosphere and according to a theory widely held for many years, this explains why the earth's atmosphere contains such a lot of oxygen. (The only plausible rival theory is that water molecules in the atmosphere are dissociated by the short-wave energy of the sun, the oxygen remaining in the Martian air and the hydrogen flying off into space.)

Thus the virtual absence of oxygen in the atmosphere of Mars can be explained on the assumption that none of the vegetation has been buried unoxidized after death, possibly because of the scarcity of water; and incidentally it follows that future colonists will find no coal or oil below ground. But if we accept Strughold's suggestion, we still have to explain how surplus oxygen stored in the young plants can be transformed to the dying ones to help them to decay. Are animals the answer? It seems to me that Strughold, having made such an ingenious suggestion, might well have followed it through to its logical conclusion.

Let's follow through on this suggestion and see where this leads. It appears intriguing to assume that some sort of animal life may be available on Mars to promote the oxidation of the dying plants. But what form do these animals take? Obviously they cannot be anything similar to animals on the earth. At the pressure on the surface of Mars our terrestrial animals would have extreme difficulty; in fact, it may be impossible for them to breathe and survive even if the entire atmosphere were oxygen. Certainly the hypothetical animals of which we speak would have had to be evolved under the low pressures present on the surface of Mars. From this analysis a metabolism based on gaseous oxygen is ruled out.

Because of the presence of so much nitrogen we might speculate on a biochemistry based in a large measure on this element, and further postulate that the adaptive processes so common to animals operates on Mars to permit life under extremely low pressures. This of course leads us into a blind alley. Water is also important, but we can imagine that these animals have no need of free water but are like the kangaroo rat of our deserts, which obtains water from the plant life in his environment. In the desert there are only three or four days of rain a year, but it is enough for the plants which are essentially hygroscopic. And in the same plant life he may obtain some free oxygen, as well as the oxygen which may be released by an internal dissociation of water. Once a creature has eaten and digested this plant life, the oxygen has been freed to go back to the atmosphere, and the cycle can start again.

During the long Martian winter there is no growth of vegetation, and the surface becomes latent. Life, we may assume, is there, but the intense cold prevents the normal metabolic processes. What do animals do under these conditions?

There are a number of low-order organisms which can survive for a considerable period of time without oxygen. Strughold points out these are to be found in ice-covered ponds or lakes. In Lake Mendota, Wisconsin, abundant life of this sort is found, but due to a lack of oxygen it is in a state of rigor. Apparently these organisms can almost completely stop their metabolism so that they need no oxygen to survive. Creatures adapted to the Martian surface conditions should possess the following qualifications: They must be either cold-blooded or of the hibernating variety so that, when the temperature drops to the point where there is insufficient food at the end of the growing season, these animals will hibernate or go into a state of suspended animation. They should be equipped with powerful limbs to burrow deep beneath the ground to escape the killing cold of the night. The temperature in the burrows should be above freezing. Also they may go into a daily hibernation as well as the annual hibernation. There appear excellent reasons why this should be a favorable condition. It would permit the almost complete stoppage of metabolic processes during the Martian night, when the temperature has dropped to a low level. In that way if there should be the availability of an oxygen reservoir, it will not be consumed during the night. The presence of a fur coat may provide further insurance against the cold and permit some activity at dawn and twilight. They must be extremely small, so that large quantities of food (with its contained oxygen and water vapor) are unnecessary. This, too, is found in the case of the small kangaroo rat, which leads a solitary life except at mating times. The desert environment will not support communal centers, so none exist. It may be assumed that they are also prolific to provide the necessary numbers to cope with the vegetation available.

It is interesting to speculate on a biological system in which there are no lungs and no breathing and in which the kidneys will not only cleanse the blood but impart to it the necessary oxygen generated from the food supply and directed to the blood under pressure. In this event the metabolism of the creature must be of low order, since it is difficult to see how enough oxygen can be ingested or created to permit the creature a metabolism similar to that of the same-sized terrestrial animal. Another reason why breathing may be a disadvantage is the narcotic effect of nitrogen. Imagine a race of breathing creatures using a 96 per cent nitrogen gas. These creatures, by our standards, would be perpetually drunk!

There is considerable evidence that a vegetable life is present on Mars. There is no evidence that animal life can exist there; in fact, all evidence indicates that animal life could not have developed to a high order on this planet. If there is animal life there, we can be assured that it did not evolve along the same pattern as on the earth. It would have had to adapt to the peculiar conditions of Mars. What about the rest of the solar system; what about life elsewhere in the universe? This has become a fascinating study in which scientists of many disciplines have played a role. To attempt the answer to this question we must retrace our steps through time to see how this all came about. First we must look into the origin of things—of the universe, of the earth, and of the solar system; of life itself.

7

In the Beginning

There is a magnificent arrogance in man's attempt to discover the origin of the universe, the evolution of the solar system, and the beginning of life on this earth. Nothing fires the imagination so intensely as speculations along these lines. Earthbound and without hope of observing other planetary systems, man strives to pierce the veil of past time for a glimpse of the mechanism that brought forth the planets, the satellites, the asteroids, the incalculable grains of dust that float among them, and the biota found on the surfaces of some of the planets.

Ingenious Dr. George Gamow of George Washington University and his colleagues have assembled an exciting, brilliant theory on the creation of the universe, not from nothing, but from some elemental fluid incredibly foreign to matter as we know it today. Gamow believes that a long time ago, perhaps five or six thousand million years ago, there existed a large cloud of an extraordinarily fantastic material which he calls "Ylem"—a word meaning the primordial material of which the elements were fashioned.

No attempt is made to reason how this "parent" of the universe came into being; it is simply assumed to have been present in that long ago. The physical nature of Ylem was so incredible as to transcend our everyday experience of space and matter.

The Ylem consisted primarily of radiation. It would have to be radiation, for the temperature, many billions of degrees, was much too high for the build-up of the atomic nuclei. As fast as nuclei were formed, they were shattered by the intense X rays and gamma rays. This was not just ordinary high-energy radiation but a radiation so dense that *a spoonful of it would weigh as much as a block of ice a half-mile on a side!*

Under these temperature conditions there was little matter, and what little there was, was composed a turmoil of neutrons, protons, and electrons—the elementary particles from which all elements are formed. Actually neutrons made up the bulk of this chaotic porridge, and the other primary particles only fitted into the picture through the disintegration of the neutrons by fast collisions sparked by the intense heat.

In that long-ago time, for a reason perhaps never to be revealed, there occurred a titanic explosion and this material was blasted from the focus with a speed approaching that of light. With the explosion the radiation, and what particles there were, raced through the universe. The temperature fell—precipitously. The particles rushed around swiftly, wildly, with speeds comparable only to those generated in today's giant cyclotrons or atom smashers. The intense radiation and the high speed of the primary particles prevented the build-up of the heavier nuclei. Five minutes after the explosion the temperature had fallen to about a billion degrees, and out of the radiation the primary particles, the lighter elements, were being fashioned. First hydrogen with its isotopes, deuterium and tritium, then helium, lithium, and so on. The step-by-step relentless building-up process of the atomic elements accelerated as the temperatures dropped low enough to permit nuclear reactions to take place without further disruption.

At the end of the first half-hour all the elements had come into being. This time scale had to be extremely and uncomfortably short, for neutrons are radioactive and disintegrate spontaneously. The half-life of neutrons is about 13 minutes, which means that if you have a pound of neutrons now, 13 minutes later you will have a half pound; 13 minutes after that you will have a quarter pound, and so on. For this reason the elements had to be fashioned in the first half-hour, when the neutrons were in still plentiful supply. It was in that first 30 minutes that the elements donned their electron raiment.

At the end of that first half-hour more than half—55 per cent—of the universe consisted of hydrogen. Helium, with 44 per cent, was the next most plentiful element, and all the other 90 elements comprised the remaining 1 per cent. Curiously, most scientists believe this same proportion of elements is present through the length and breadth of space today.

Even with the complete build-up of the atomic species the universe continued expanding and the temperature continued falling. There came a time when nothing of importance was happening in the universe. Finally the melting points of some of the heavier elements were reached, and they began condensing out of the gas. The temperature continued dropping—and now, instead of a pure gas expanding, there were mixed in with the gas the solid grains of the elements which exist in the solid state under normal terrestrial conditions.

For 30 million years, Dr. Gamow assumes, the expansion persisted and the temperatures fell until at the end of that time the temperature had fallen to 80 degrees F. The universe which had been one of fierce radiation had become one of inert matter! Everything was dark, still, cold, and silent. The stage was now set for the next act in the creation drama.

The Stars Come into Being

In any violent explosion some of the expelled particles are set spinning. Events were not different at the dawn of time in the exploding universe. Some of the clouds of gases from which evolved the galaxies such as our own Milky Way system were set spinning, and these evolved as concrete entities in which the masses of these protogalaxies was billions of times that of our sun. These contracted, and the spin accelerated. Certain shear stresses were set up in each protogalaxy until the cloud assumed a flat, rough pancake form in which the edge became the arms of the spiral galaxy.

At the same time other events were occurring. There was an inherent turbulence in the protogalaxies, which gave rise to eddies which collided, intermingled, bumped, increased density, and massed together until sizable clouds of spinning, cold particles and gas formed. With the passage of time these smaller spinning gas clouds began to shrink under their own gravitational fields. There was a rise in pressure due to the compression of the gases, and finally at some point in the process the surfaces of these amorphous masses began to glow. Radiation—light—had come back to the universe. The compressions continued until finally the central temperatures of these gaseous bodies had reached ten to 20 million degrees. The stars were born. The thermonuclear fires had been lit; the transformation of hydrogen into helium became possible; the clouds of gas were now stars to speed their light to the remotest corner of the universe.

Two hundred million years had elapsed since the creation of the universe! The stage was now set for the evolution of the solar system.

The Evolution of the Solar System

Speculation on the origin of the solar system began in ancient times. But only since the discovery of the telescope with its revolutionary impact on scientific thought have the observational data for analysis become available. So all ideas, proposals, schemes, and hypotheses date from the middle of the seventeenth century when the French philosopher René Descartes made the first attempt to explain the observed order and regularities in the solar system without the assumption of a divine creation.

The similarities in the solar system are too numerous for the sun to have captured the planets one by one. It is inconceivable that such regularity could be accidental.

Therefore the scientist looks for a logical orderly sequence to explain what is found in the system.

The planets all move in a narrow belt in the sky called the zodiac. As observed from the north pole of the sky their motions are all counterclockwise. Except for some distant ones which for dynamical reasons revolve in the opposite direction the satellites or moons also revolve around the planets in counterclockwise directions. Any explanation of the formation of these bodies must explain the revolutions of the planets and the moons.

The planets all turn with various periods, but the spin is, with one known exception, from west to east, or counterclockwise as viewed from the north pole of the sky. From the earth we see the stars, sun, and moon all rise in the east and set in the west because the earth rotates or spins on its axis from west to east. The other planets, too, while each has its own spin period, turn from west to east, or counterclockwise as seen from the north pole of the sky, with one known exception—Uranus. (We do not know the direction of rotation of Pluto.) The axis of Uranus is lying down, so to speak, and as a result does not rotate in the same fashion as the other planets. A theory must explain this odd position of the poles of rotation of Uranus.

Finally there is the problem of the angular momentum of the planets. The angular momentum is the product of many things. It is affected by the spin of the planet on its axis, the mass of the planet, its distance from the sun which contains the center of gravity for the solar system, and finally by its year or time to circuit the sun once. Fast spin, great distance, and large mass increase the angular momentum.

From this it is apparent that the planets possess most of the angular momentum of the solar system because of the great mass of the major planets, their rapid days, and their great distance from the sun.

The planets, with less than two tenths of 1 per cent of the mass or material of the solar system, have 98 per cent of the angular momentum, while the sun, with more than 99 per cent of the mass, possesses but 2 per cent of the angular momentum. Jupiter alone has about 60 per cent of the angular momentum, while the four inner planets, from Mercury through Mars, have only about a fifth of 1 per cent. There must be a logical explanation for these facts, if we are to believe that the sun and the planets are really a family.

While for three centuries there have been speculations concerning the origin of the system, only recently have there been developed the analytical tools to tackle the problem. The old theories were highly ingenious, but quite untenable both qualitatively and quantitatively. However, from a historical point of view it is interesting that the first major theory, which was popular for a considerable period, is now returning to favor, albeit in modern dress.

The idea that the sun was once a huge spinning ball of hot, seething, incandescent gas contracting under gravitational forces and leaving behind, as it grew smaller, rings of matter from which the planets evolved is one of the oldest theories of the formation of the system and is at the same time at the core of the newest theory. The German philosopher Immanuel Kant first proposed the evolution of the system from gas rings, back in 1755; the great French geometer Pierre Simon de Laplace in 1796 applied mathematics to the theory.

The nebular hypothesis of the Marquis de Laplace called for a ring of matter in the plane of the sun's equator. As the sun continued to rotate and contract, in accordance with well-established laws of dynamics, it had to rotate faster to preserve a constant angular momentum. In the same fashion a skater, beginning a whirl, holds his arms outstretched and keeps them there until he gets up to speed. Once he attains speed, he suddenly pulls his arms in tightly, and his spin grows very much faster.

The skater demonstrates the principle of the conservation of angular momentum. He has a certain inherent spin. When his arms are outstretched, the weight of these parts of his body is farther from his center of gravity, and so his speed must be slower to account for the distribution of weight. But when his weight is concentrated, close to his center of gravity (in order to maintain his angular momentum), he must spin faster.

As the nebula contracted, the rotational speed increased, and the rim of the disc-shaped nebula moved faster and faster. Finally the spin became so rapid that the centrifugal force exceeded the gravitational attraction of the nebula, and the rings began to detach. The rings would be left behind very much like rings on water around the splash of a stone in a quiet pond and they would consolidate into planets at the correct distances from the sun.

This nebular hypothesis enjoyed a unique position for almost a century, though in 1859 the English physicist

Clerke Maxwell developed mathematical proofs to show that the rings could never condense into a single body. He proved they would form a stable configuration of tiny particles much like the rings around the planet Saturn. The nebular hypothesis failed also to account for the inequality of angular momentum in the sun and planets and the fact that the sun should spin faster. However, for want of a better theory, Laplace's ideas persisted to the twentieth century.

The twentieth century, so far, has been a period of jockeying between the gradual evolutionary process of the solar system, as outlined by the nebular hypothesis, and its formation by a cataclysmic action. Only with the beginning of the twentieth century came the unveiling of the exciting scientific drama of an encounter between the sun and another star.

In 1895 two University of Chicago scientists, T. C. Chamberlain and F. R. Moulton, proposed the "Planetesimal Hypothesis." They proposed that long ago there was an intruder, a "father" star which passed within three million miles of the sun. As the speeding star approached, giant tides piled up on the surface of the sun, much like the tides raised in the oceans of the earth by the gravitational action of the sun and the moon, but millions of times higher. These tides became so high that the sun became unstable and could regain its equilibrium only by throwing off a huge, hot "filament" of matter, possibly 5000 million miles long.

The matter thus ripped from the sun in a colossal cloud cooled and condensed into particles of dust, called "planetesimals" and little droplets of liquid. The savage internal motion of the particles was random, so there were innumerable collisions. As the particles collided, they grew by accretion and finally formed the planets. The planetesimal mechanism could explain most of the regularities of the solar system but it could not account for the unreasonable angular momentum of Jupiter.

During the First World War two English scientists, Sir James Jeans and Sir Harold Jeffreys, refined the calculations and showed that a part of the sun could not be detached by tidal action alone. Their researches showed that an actual shearing collision was necessary for matter to be torn from the sun.

The filament, blasted from the sun by the sidewiping action of the intruder star, was imagined to be cigar-shaped. With less material in the ends than in the middle of the cigar, the smaller planets are found close to and most distant from the sun. In the center, where the concentration of matter was greatest, the major planets of the solar system were born. Here are found the planets Jupiter, Saturn, Uranus, and Neptune. The metamorphosis from a glob of gas to an earth with a hot crust Dr. Jeffreys calculates as taking about a million years.

Again in this theory the great handicap to its acceptance was the tremendous inequality in the angular momentum distributed in the solar system. By no stretch of the imagination could an encounter between two stars give rise to a system where 98 per cent of the angular momentum resides outside the sun.

To overcome this objection Dr. R. A. Lyttleton—then a student of America's dean of astronomers, Henry Norris Russell—postulated the sun as one member of a twin-star system. The intruder star could then pull, from the other star, "planet matter" which would be captured by the sun, and this could have enough angular momentum to satisfy the situation as we know it today.

While at the time this appeared to be a solution, it was exceedingly short lived. In 1939 Dr. Lyman Spitzer, Jr., now director of the Princeton Observatory, showed that if matter were pulled from the sun or another star, it would have a temperature of several million degrees. At this high temperature the matter would not condense into planets as was supposed but would explode violently into the vacuum of space, and the radiation pressure of the sun would finish the job by blasting the gas out as a nebula. The explosion of the solar material would be very much like the blowing of a smoke ring into an electric fan. Thus ended all hopes for an explanation through a cataclysmic action.

In 1944 the German astronomer Carl von Weizsacher investigated the behavior of a large cloud of dust and gas around a massive body like the sun. Here was the completion of a cycle, for this was, in part, a return to the Kant Hypothesis.

Weizsacher imagined the sun plunging through a comparatively dense interstellar cloud of gas and dust. On photographs of the sky there are hundreds of these nebulae which we discover only because they obscure the stars or bright nebulae behind them. Many are so enormous that the sun with a speed of 12 miles per second would need several hundred thousand years to plow through one! Because of gravitational attraction the sun would gather enormous quantities of nebular material and gradually evolve a giant rotating nebula of its own. Internal friction and centrifugal forces would shape this material into a disk with a diameter comparable to the present diameter of the solar system—say 8000 or 10,000 millions of miles—and a final thickness of about 200 million miles.

Weizsacher showed that the planets could be formed from such a nebula in something like 100 million years. The solar nebula was supposed to have possessed a mass of about a tenth that of the sun. Most of the lighter gases, such as hydrogen and helium, would have boiled away, and only the remaining heavy elements, the 1 per cent, would go into making the dust particles. These would accrete to form the embryo planets and give them a composition completely different from that of the stars.

The stimulating contribution of Weizsacher is the discovery that any spinning system, be it a gas or a cloud of dust and gas, creates a turbulence which produces eddies or whirlpools throughout the entire nebula. Draw a canoe paddle strongly and quickly through the water and you produce the same thing: dozens of little whirlpools of various sizes.

By applying the theories of turbulence Weizsacher showed that at the boundaries of the eddies, because the inner parts of the nebula rotated faster than the outside, the dust coagulated most rapidly. Following well-understood laws, Weizsacher also showed that the boundaries would be spaced in approximately a geometrical progression from the sun in just the order in which the planets are observed. This theory advanced the conditioned dream about the earth's creation a long way, but it was not the final step.

While Weizsacher's nebular theory accounted for more observational data than any other up to that time, it was already dated by the wealth of research material emerging from wind tunnels and aeronautical laboratories. New theories and new data came particularly from the German physicist Werner Heisenberg and the Russian mathematician A. N. Kolmogoroff; and the man who applied them to the theory of the formation of the solar system is brilliant, dynamic Dr. Kuiper.

Dr. Kuiper may well be setting the stage for the last act in this cosmic drama, for by using this latest information he has shown that turbulence would not produce rings of similar eddies as proposed by Weizsacher. Instead, Kuiper imagines a series of single super-eddies at prescribed distances from the sun, thus accounting for the observed spacing of the planets. His work discloses that a solar nebula would form an entire "spectrum" or sequence of various-sized eddies ranging from microscopic ones to others millions of miles in extent. He shows further that the large eddies would devour or absorb the smaller ones until, after something like 100 million years, the eddies would consolidate into relatively few big ones. From these gigantic clouds of primordial "planet stuff" Kuiper believes the planets did, in fact, develop.

Here again, as in the Weizsacher concept, the solar nebula was assumed to contain about a tenth as much stuff as the sun, and of this enormous amount of material only 1 per cent is to be found in the planets. All the other material, principally the lightest gases, hydrogen and helium, escaped into space. This latest theory also explains the relatively small amount of the lighter gases in most of the planets. However, in the larger planets, which have low temperatures and strong gravitational fields, these light gases are held or captured. This accounts for methane and ammonia in the atmosphere of Jupiter and Saturn and for hydrogen and methane on Uranus and Neptune. Both methane and ammonia are hydrogen compounds.

The smaller planets are made of solid material with only an insignificant amount of gas clinging to the surface as an envelope or atmosphere. The earth, the obvious example, has a density of 5.5 times water, Venus 4.9, Mercury 3.8, while the large planets are so light that, for example, were there an ocean big enough to hold Saturn (density 0.7), the planet would float.

Unfortunately neither the Weizsacher nor Kuiper theory makes any attempt to account for the angular momentum of Jupiter. Dr. Kuiper indicates that the problem of the peculiar distribution of angular momentum is an almost universal one in stellar systems. Any place you find double or multiple stars, and fully half the stars in the sky are such, you find this mystery. He believes the slow solar rotation is a universal condition among all stars like the sun and requires a separate solution. This is the only missing link in the most difficult of the present-day cosmic puzzles.

Among the interesting later steps in the development of the system must be mentioned the possibility that the asteroids, or minor planets which circle the sun largely between the orbits of Mars and Jupiter, originated in the cataclysmic destruction of one of the original planets. Meteorites, too, may represent the smaller fragments of the debris. Another probably postorigin development is the capture of smaller bodies by some of the large planets. The outer satellites of Jupiter and Saturn revolve around their primaries in the "wrong" direction. Dynamical studies show that satellites at those distances from their primaries would have very unstable orbits if they revolved in the common west-to-east direction, whereas their stability in retrograde orbits is considerably higher. But to have retrograde orbits almost certainly indicates that they were later captures, and not original satellites. In all probability the planet Pluto, out on the known fringe of the system, is an escaped satellite of Neptune, and not one of the original planets, whereas Triton, the larger satellite of Neptune, may be a captured body, inasmuch as its motion is retrograde.

And of course there has been considerable evolution of the earth's atmosphere. Originally there was present methane, ammonia and water. As time went on, the ultraviolet radiation of the sun and the continuous lightning present at that time, due to the turbulent convection currents in the atmosphere, oxidized the methane into carbon dioxide, dissociated the water into hydrogen and oxygen and broke down the ammonia into hydrogen and nitrogen. Hydrogen, the lightest of the elements, soon escaped from the earth, but carbon dioxide, oxygen, and nitrogen remained and compose the atmosphere today.

While this appears to be a simple story, the details are quite complex and in many cases vague, but the broad outlines are believed to be understood today. For one thing the heat of the earth, as it grew hotter by radioactive decay, broke down the water of crystallization in the rocks, and this water issued from the volcanoes to be added to the atmosphere. Tremendous amounts of carbon dioxide were taken out of circulation and locked into tiny marine organisms which inhabited the earth in vast untold numbers. Limestone was deposited in great quantities in the earth's history. When plant life evolved on the earth, suddenly a new and powerful source of oxygen became available. In fact, many scientists believe the oxygen content of our atmosphere is of secondary origin coming from the photosynthesis mechanism evolved by our flora. But even with all of these factors operating it is apparent to the scientist that our atmosphere has not undergone significant change in the past five or six thousand million years.

8

↑

Life in the Universe

Throughout most intellectual history it has been assumed that the origin of life was a mystery that must forever lie outside human understanding. In recent times it has been the belief that, while not supernatural, the event that marked the transition from the inanimate to the living in the earth's remote past must yet defy disclosure by the methods of science.

Astronomers might build their universes and people them with stars and barren planets. Biologists were at liberty to reconstruct the evolution of the complex creatures of today from the earliest imaginable things that had the power to reproduce their kind. It has been the custom to admire the products of the brains that have given us the two sequences of evolution—the development of the physical world and the development of the living world—without insistence on the impossible. To build a sound bridge between the two worlds seemed impossible.

But suddenly this picture has changed. Nobelist Harold C. Urey and his colleague Stanley L. Miller, at the University of Chicago, have succeeded in synthesizing the amino acids, the building blocks of the protein molecule which is the basis of all living matter.

Protein is made up of about 25 different amino acids. All animals and all plants—in short, all living cells—are made up of them, wholly or in part. We cannot conceive of any living organism which does not contain them. The jellylike substance found inside all living things, the protoplasm, is made up of proteins and water. And in Dr. Urey's laboratory the basic components of protein were synthesized.

Let's go back to the beginning of this work. In 1952 at the G. H. Jones Chemical Laboratory of the University of Chicago, Miller assembled a rather simple apparatus for the simulation of conditions which existed thousands of millions of years ago.

Essentially the system was a closed one. A solution of one part water with two parts ammonia and two parts methane was brought to the boiling point, after many tests were made to preclude contamination by living organisms. The vapors rose and passed into a rather large bulb. The pressure of the gases then drove these vapors down and past an electric discharge from a spark coil similar to the one in your automobile, after which they dropped into a cooling chamber where the vapors were liquified and the cycle began again.

Here, indeed, was the simulation of what had taken place on the earth in the long ago. These were the three compounds present in the atmosphere of the earth when it cooled, and the electric discharge was essentially the same mechanism as the short-wave radiations from the sun or the lightning discharges of that time.

After about a week during which time the vapors circulated continuously through the strong electric discharge, the brew turned from a light pink to a deep muddy red. The products of this experiment were then analyzed by a new technique called paper chromatography, and they verified that the mixture contained some of the amino acids.

The amino acids definitely identified were glycine, alpha-alanine, beta alanine, sarcosine, valine, and two others—aspartic and butyric acids—present only in traces. Actually there are probably others, for about 20 spots on the paper strips remain to be identified; but if they are there, they are present in such minute quantities that it was impossible to identify them.

The protein molecules probably contain 25 different amino acids, and here more than 25 per cent were synthesized!

The curious thing about this experiment is that it permits scientists to trace the beginnings of life back far beyond the previous time scales.

While life has been generally assumed to have come to the earth some 2.5 thousand million years ago it may now be assumed to have occurred long before that epoch. The scientists point out that only in the early history of the earth were there the ammonia, methane, and water vapor in the atmosphere which could give rise to the amino acids! But make no mistake, amino acids are not life; they are as far removed from protein molecules as a few blocks of stone are from a castle. And, what is even more significant, the protein molecule is even farther removed from a single living cell.

If the universe is assumed to have come into existence some six thousand million years ago, then 5.8 thousand million years ago conditions were right for the production of the amino acids. Urey indicates that if only half the present surface carbon dioxide in the form of organic compounds had been dissolved in waters that comprise 10 per cent of the present oceans, the ancient oceans would have possessed approximately a 10 per cent soup of organic compounds. Had there also existed a primeval chemist, he would have found on analyzing these primeval waters such elementary compounds as alcohol, vinegar, formaldehyde, and others of this type. This, the scientist considered a favorable situation for the beginning of life.

If this is the picture, we can well believe that in that long-ago time when the rocks were still hot; when the greatest continuous storm of all time—the 1000-year thunderstorm—raged unabated; when there occurred alternate periods of bright sunshine with its intense short-wave radiation and darkness with its fluid lightning; and when the air and sea seethed with a complex chemical turbulence—*then* it was that the shadowy beginnings of life may have taken form. For the next three thousand million years the elemental components of life moved with the pulse of the sea, seeking the right combination for the creation of the protein molecule we know today. Untold years must then have elapsed until the right combination of protein molecules was assembled into a unique pattern to form the living cell.

Somewhere, sometime, more than 2.5 thousand million

years ago, the complex living cells materialized, and life had arrived on the earth. Carbon specks, the remains of a most primitive form of life, are found in the rocks estimated to be 2.5 thousand million years old. From that time on the progress up the evolutionary ladder proceeded at an accelerated pace until today we find man at the very summit.

So it was that life came to this earth, and the sentient creatures which abound thereon now gaze into the sky and ask themselves the eternal question: Is there life elsewhere?

Down through the ages this query was posed to philosophers, as we called the scientists of old, and to the present-day man of science. And of all these scientists, those in the realm of astronomy who have spread across other disciplines are in the best position to assess the evidence for the answer. It is the astronomer who has projected his sights off the earth to the other celestial bodies. Using all the physical sciences at his command, he has studied and observed the close neighbors of the earth and has explored their histories and present conditions for an answer. Too well does the astronomer know that if other life is to be found and observed, it must be present in our own solar system. The universe is so big we cannot even see the planets that almost certainly revolve around many of the other stars, let alone the life that may infest these planets in almost infinite number and variety. So the attention of the combination astronomer and biologist—or, as Dr. Otto Struve calls this peculiar individual, the astro-biologist—is brought into sharp focus on our own planetary system.

The Search for Life

In the search for life on other worlds it should be remembered that the only living things we could identify on a visit to other planets would be recognizable creatures to which we are accustomed. It may be perfectly possible that there may exist forms of life unrecognizable even if we were in their midst. So obviously our discussion must be limited to recognizable living things. For this "life like ours" it is possible to establish certain criteria.

The first is that of time. The author has never seen this point raised in discussions on life but he considers it significant enough to merit comment. The writer can imagine a planet somewhere in space where there are creatures which have a life span equivalent to a million of our years. These strange creatures get around very slowly. Perhaps they move by growing some sort of support in front and having the rear projections atrophy and drop off. Nevertheless this can be considered a form of locomotion.

Now suppose that we were to examine these creatures for an hour, a day, a week, or even a year. We might not detect any sign of life, and if there were the slightest sign of change, we might consider it an inorganic change similar to the ones we see taking place all around us on the earth. Under these conditions it would be unlikely that we would call these creatures animate.

Yet if we could explode our time scale so that 70 earth years could be transformed into a million years, we might see these objects behaving in a normal manner; that is, normal to us on the exploded time scale.

On the other hand there may be creatures living on the

earth which have a short life. The writer can imagine creatures which in a fraction of a second are born, live their
lives, die, and are instantly devoured by microbes or bac-
teria. In this brief instant they have lived their lives and
are followed by their descendants.

Now if we could telescope our lives so that our 70 years
becomes a fraction of a second, we would see these creatures behaving in a manner which to us would be normal.

From this it is apparent that one of the important criteria is the presence of a compatible time scale.

When you look into the night sky, with an excellent
pair of eyes and under the very best observing conditions,
you may count several thousand stars. These stars possess
surface temperatures ranging from 2500 to 100,000 degrees. If we could dig down beneath the surfaces, we might
find temperatures which would reach several hundred million degrees.

Between the stars the temperature is a few degrees above
the absolute zero! This is about 460 degrees below zero on
the Fahrenheit scale. This means that there is an enormous range of temperatures in the observable universe.
Yet in this entire range there is only a tiny, narrow hair's-
breadth in which life like ours can exist. At the most, life
is confined to the range between 100 degrees below zero
and 200 above!

There is good reason for this narrow restriction. If the
temperature rises too high, the water in the body cells will
evaporate. The cells will become dessicated and die. Life
is known to be made up of giant, complex organic molecules, and it is known that high temperatures can readily
break up or destroy these giant molecules, in turn causing

death. It has been estimated that if the average daily temperature on the earth fluctuated 20 degrees either way, all human life would perish.

The action of these large, complex protein molecules—called enzymes—under high temperatures governs the possibility of life. These enzymes permit body reactions to take place at a given rate for a lower temperature. Raise the temperature and the reaction rates increase. But the enzymes are unstable and go to irreversible destruction when subjected to excessive heat. Therefore if the temperature goes up high enough, life cannot continue.

Run the temperature down too low and the water will crystallize and freeze out. Again under these conditions the cells will die. From this it is readily seen that for recognizable life the temperature must be moderate.

Water is also necessary for life and the perpetuation of life. Wherever we expect to find life we must find water vapor and in copious quantities. Take the human body as an example; 70 per cent of it is water. A man can go for several weeks without food but only for a few days without water. Water is ingested in greater amounts than all other substances and by the same token it is the chief excretion.

It is the character of water which has led it to become so important to life. It has, for instance, an unusually high specific heat—that is, it heats up slowly but once hot is stingy about giving up its heat. This results in a tendency to maintain nearly constant temperatures. Life is directly favored by this property, because a given amount of heat will produce little change in the body temperature. As an example, a 165-pound man produces about 2400 calories daily, which would be sufficient to raise his temperature about 58 degrees if he were not constantly radiating heat to his surroundings. But if his body did not possess its high water content, the temperature rise would be in excess of 250 degrees, and radiation might not be able to keep the body at the normal efficient temperature of 98.6 degrees F.

It is what is called the high latent heat of water which makes it an ideal regulating mechanism to keep the body temperature of the living organism stable. No less striking is water as the universal solvent and as having the highest surface tension except for mercury. All living organisms are colloidal, which means the cells are suspended in a liquid, and water is the principle constituent of the liquid.

The last criterion for life is the presence of an atmosphere with a substantial amount of oxygen. Oxygen is necessary for many reasons, the principal one being the oxidation of the food we eat to provide energy for the body. Through the medium of the blood stream it furnishes the cells with the oxygen necessary for energy production in the body. It functions also for purifying the body of the waste products of the metabolic processes.

So critical are these qualifications that all conditions must be fulfilled. It is inconceivable that life could continue if even one of the criteria was not met in a reasonable measure. And now that the conditions for life have been set forth, let's turn our attention to other planets, to see if life could exist there.

Sir William Herschel at one time believed there was life on the sun. He imagined the hot visible layers of the sun as an upper atmosphere not affecting the solar creatures. That idea has long since been disproved, but it is interesting to note that the foremost astronomer of his era could be completely in error on this idea. Soon after Herschel it was generally accepted that only the planets could harbor life. These are the bodies we have been able to observe critically because we are able to train giant telescopes and other powerful scientific instruments on them. We can compare their surface conditions to those on the earth and thus permit intelligent speculation on whether a life like ours might exist on them.

The planet closest to the sun is Mercury. It is the smallest planet in the solar system and because it is the closest to the sun it is the fastest moving. Because Mercury is one third as far from the sun as the earth, it receives nine times as much energy and must therefore be hot. Actually, directly underneath the sun the temperature gets up to 750 degrees! At this temperature lead and tin would be molten. However, away from this subsolar point the temperature drops off markedly, and there should be places near the limb which have temperatures approximating those of the temperate zone on the earth.

Because this planet rotates on its axis in the same length of time it takes it to swing around the sun, there is one side of Mercury which never receives sunlight, and thus it must be bitterly cold on this side. Temperatures, as we have discovered, are a factor, but not the only one which governs the possibility of life on the planet. Mercury is so small that if it ever had an atmosphere—and we are certain that at one time it did—that atmosphere has long since vanished into space. The gravitational field of the planet is too weak to retain an atmosphere. For these reasons Mercury can be ruled out as an abode of life.

The next planet out is Venus. It is twice as far from the sun as is Mercury, and so its temperature is not so high, but it is still higher than that of the earth. Venus is about the same size as the earth and so it has, like the earth, an atmosphere. In fact, the atmosphere on Venus is so dense that we have never seen its surface. The only substance which the astronomer has analyzed on the planet is carbon dioxide.

Carbon dioxide is an insidious stuff. It will let in the radiation of the sun but will not let it out. Therefore the surface temperature should be higher than it would be without the carbon dioxide in the atmosphere. Actually there is considerable speculation on the temperature, though it probably lies somewhere between 140 and 212 degrees F. While these high temperatures may mean that animals like those on the earth cannot survive, it is possible for an animal to adapt to the high temperature. On the earth organisms are found in the hot springs which live in temperatures of 180 degrees F.

But Venus has become prominent recently for another reason. Drs. Menzel and Whipple of the Harvard College Observatory have proposed a most plausible theory for the presence of water vapor on Venus. In fact, they feel that perhaps there is considerable water in the clouds and on the surface of Venus.

Let's see what the background of this situation is. Astronomers of the Mt. Wilson Observatory in their measures on Venus found that the total amount of water vapor above the clouds of Venus did not exceed 2 to 5 per cent of that in the earth's atmosphere above Mt. Wilson. This, it was believed, was evidence that the planet's atmosphere did not contain enough water to account for the clouds.

However, the Mt. Wilson astronomers based their data on an analysis of the spectrum of Venus. As in the case of the measures on Mars, the light is really sunlight which has penetrated the atmosphere and is then reflected to the observer on the earth. It was found that the light coming from Venus is reflected from great altitudes. It has been determined that at this altitude the temperature is about 38 degrees below zero. It is well known that the cooler a given parcel of air the less moisture it can retain. A moisture-saturated atmosphere in motion from the surface up having this temperature should contain less than 2 per cent of the water vapor above Mt. Wilson at a comparable temperature. Thus failure to detect appreciable quantities of water by spectral analysis of Venus, it would appear, does not preclude the possibility that the planet's clouds *are composed of water vapor.*

Further, these astronomers advanced reasonable evidence which suggests the entire surface of Venus is, in fact, an ocean—an ocean uninterrupted by continental land masses. They point out that Venus' predominantly carbon-dioxide atmosphere could not exist if land masses were exposed to it, since under these conditions the carbon dioxide would combine chemically in the presence of water with silicates in the rocks to form carbonates. A water layer covering the land would preclude this chemical compounding and permit free carbon dioxide to remain in the atmosphere, as is evident. Thus water can be assumed in the atmosphere of Venus.

Given the presence of water, carbon dioxide, and the

radiations of the sun, it is conceivable that life could have
started there. It may very well be that there is abundant
life, both animal and vegetable, though it may be aquatic
in nature. While this is a highly involved and fascinating
speculation concerning the planet, the very fact that it has
its opaque cloud cover precludes our uncovering the entire
story until such time as space travelers reach Venus and
penetrate to its surface. At this time Venus, and not Mars,
appears to be the planet of mystery.

The largest planet in the solar system is Jupiter. It has
a gravitational field 2.6 times that of the earth. Therefore
it can readily retain an atmosphere, even of hydrogen.
However, the point about Jupiter and the more distant
planets—Saturn, Uranus, Neptune, and Pluto—is that they
are so far from the sun. Jupiter is five times as far from
the sun as is the earth and thus it receives one twenty-fifth
as much energy as does the earth. For this reason Jupiter
should be very cold, and observationally this is found to
be true. The temperature on the top of the cloud belts on
Jupiter is 200 degrees below zero; that is colder than dry
ice. If there were a place to land on this planet, which
there is not, the extreme cold temperature would make
the evolution of life impossible.

In addition to the extreme cold encountered on these
outer planets there is also the problem of an atmosphere
for humans. Let us suppose that some time in the distant
future men will be able to get to these outer planets. Will
they be able to live if they could protect themselves against
the extreme cold? They would also have to guard themselves against the noxious gases which they would find on
the planets. Out there methane, ammonia, helium, and

hydrogen are in abundance. All of these in concentrated doses are unhealthy.

That is all there is to the solar system except one planet, Mars, which was examined in great detail in the preceding chapters. In this system we have found that there is both animal and vegetable life on the earth. On Mars there is vegetable life, and the possibility of an animal organism of low order; we can only speculate on the possibility of both aquatic animal and vegetable life on Venus. Now where do we go from here? Can there be life elsewhere?

It is inconceivable to this writer that life exists only on the earth. He believes that in the vast reaches of the universe there is an infinity of life. Much of it may be like our very own. Some of it may be identical, and some may occur in forms that we earthlings would not recognize.

This concept of an infinity of life is based not on wild, irrational imagination but on the serious consideration that there must be other "earths" scattered through the millions of galaxies in the universe. It is true, at this time, that we cannot discover directly any planetary systems other than our own, but we do observe a phenomenon which probably points to their existence. Certain stars whose positions have been measured more or less continuously, with very high precision, are found to move along a wavy line. The astronomer knows that nothing but the gravitational attraction of another massive body can make a star deviate from straight-line motion.

The motion of a star and a major planet may be compared to an Argentinian bola being thrown through the air. Except to make the analogy closer we must imagine the two balls of unequal size—in fact, let's have one four inches in diameter and the other a tiny one, perhaps a half inch in diameter. Now when the bola is thrown, the course it takes is determined by the mass of the big ball; but if it is photographed and carefully observed, its trajectory will not be uniform but will have little wiggles in it produced by the smaller ball. The star and a massive companion behave in the same fashion.

From the size of the wiggle the astronomer can determine the mass of the dark companion in terms of the mass of the observed star. When this is done, it is found that in one case the dark companion has a mass about one sixtieth that of the bright star. This, incidentally, is the smallest of the dark companions uncovered to date.

The important point is that if there exists dark companions one sixtieth of the mass, why could there not be others with smaller masses? There is no reason why there could not be. The mechanism which gave rise to the large, dark companion can also give rise to the smaller ones. This information added to data obtained from other studies has led some astronomers to the conclusion that one star out of every hundred is accompanied by a planetary system! This means that in our own Milky Way system, our galaxy with its 100 thousand million stars, there are at least a thousand million planetary systems.

With the 200-inch telescope on Mt. Palomar the astronomer has penetrated space to a depth of at least two thousand million light-years or 12,000,000,000,000,000,000,000 miles! In this observable universe the astronomer believes there are at least a thousand million star systems or galaxies like the Milky Way. From this it is further seen that in the observable universe there must be at least a million,

million, million planetary systems containing a central star and a system of planets revolving around that star.

With spectroscopes attached to the large telescopes the astronomer finds that the same elements which are found in our part of space, near the sun, are scattered through the length and breadth of the universe and in roughly the same proportion. And also in space we find stars which are quite like our sun in size and temperature and that give off about the same amount and same type of radiation as our sun. So the conditions for the beginning of life in those distant places are not too different from those which occurred on the earth in the long ago.

I believe that out in space there are many stars like our own sun, surrounded by planetary systems identical to ours. In many if not most of those planetary systems there is a smaller planet about the size of the earth about 100 million miles from its sun. The atmosphere on that distant planet was similar to that of the earth in the long ago. Both the radiations from the sun and those induced on the planet were also similar to those found on the earth at the dawn of time. Under these conditions, with our knowing in a general way what had to take place to give rise to life here, is it not possible that there is also a life out there and of a nature similar to ours? Statistically the answer to this must be yes. There are so many places where life could have occurred and so much time available that it is inconceivable that this life on the earth is unique.

Those who will question the time available may be aware that in the modern views on the stars it is considered that stars are being born all the time from dark, cold, irregular masses of dust and gas in the galaxies. Two such stars, newly born, have been discovered in the Great Nebula of Orion within the past few years. Under these conditions it is possible to have stars which are quite old and others which are quite new. And around some of these stars are planets which are in the same state as our earth, perhaps five thousand million years ago. In the same way some stars may be scattered through space which are slightly older than the sun, and therefore there may be life around these stars which is much farther advanced than that on our planet.

APPENDIX

It's About Time

A tremendous amount has been written concerning space travel. In 1950 a survey of many qualified scientists in the field was made, and their estimates as to when we will be able to get off the earth ranged from ten to 15 years to half a century. This question was posed to the author in 1955, and the time scale he devised has been accepted by many scientists.

If the unmanned, instrumented satellite is a reality in 1957 or 1958, he believed that by 1960 the television satellite will be placed in the sky to circle the earth at an altitude of 4000 miles in a four-hour orbit. This will telemeter back to the earth weather pictures of whole continents, thus making weather predictions a good bit more accurate.

By 1964 an instrumented satellite should go up and stay for some weeks or perhaps several months. This will be the "animal" satellite, for it will contain a full complement of mice, monkeys, and guinea pigs. These creatures will be carefully observed and their psychological and physiological reactions telemetered back to the earth. A comprehensive knowledge of the behavior of these animals will pave the way for the *manned,* instrumented satellite in 1968.

Again a satellite will get into the sky but this time with a human cargo—perhaps a single man or perhaps a small group. The important and significant knowledge of the human behavior to high accelerative forces and to the weird, unearthly feeling of gravity-free space will result from this adventure. There will be one major difference between this satellite and all the others which have gone up before. This one will have to return to the earth's surface. Building on this work will come the full-scale space station to circle the earth in a two-hour orbit at 1075 miles above the surface of the earth. The space station may be erected by 1978 or 1980.

Now will come a time of consolidation—a time for restocking our scientific cupboard, and finally, by the year 2000, trips to the moon and planets are contemplated.

It can be assumed with considerable assurance that the first planet which will be visited and explored will be Mars. The choice is

147

governed by our knowledge of the surface. It is certain that from what is already known of Mars today, it will be possible to land and take off from its surface.

One of the more necessary, significant instruments which the space traveler will need will be a timepiece—a clock. This will not be a simple type of clock but a complex and accurate one to indicate time and date, on both Mars and the earth.

"Why," the reader may ask, "will this be so important?" The answer lies in the tremendous speeds involved in space travel. There will come a time on Mars when the explorer will contemplate the return to the earth-circling space station. The instant the return has been decided is the instant he must know the precise time on the earth to determine the earth satellite position so that rendezvous with it can be effected. Depending on circumstances such as fuel supply, provisions, and other minor factors, missing the space station through faulty timing may doom an expedition. For this reason the precise earth time is secondary only to fuel and supplies to any group that leaves the earth.

How do we go about building this clock? The most important items which must be completely understood and incorporated into this clock are the rotation periods, the day of the earth, and Mars. Let's begin with the earth.

The earth spins on its axis once in 23 hours, 56 minutes, 4 seconds, which we call the sidereal day. This day is reckoned from the time a particular star appears on the meridian—that is, when it is due south—to the next time that star is on the meridian. However, the day we normally refer to, the day we live, is the mean solar day— that is, the day from noon to noon. This is the 24-hour day we use in our everyday lives.

As we have already discovered, Mars rotates on its axis once in 24 hours, 37 minutes, 22.6689 seconds. However, this is the sidereal day. The solar day is 24 hours, 39 minutes, 35.16 seconds long in mean solar units. Therefore Mars rotates slower than the earth; and if they were both to start off at the same time, then when the earth had made a complete rotation, Mars would still have slightly more than 39 minutes to go. Thus the day on Mars is about 4 per cent longer than that of the earth.

Imagine that you are on Mars and you have an earth clock. It is obvious that the clock will be a poor timekeeper for Mars. For instance, on the earth we are accustomed to eating lunch at noon. We might want to follow the same pattern on Mars. However, in using the earth time we would find that lunch the following day would be about 40 minutes earlier and lunch the day after about

80 minutes earlier. In fact, go on for about 18 days and you will be having lunch at the Martian midnight. This obviously won't do. Therefore it would be best to develop a clock which will keep time on Mars.

Arbitrarily we could divide the Martian solar day into 24 hours as in the case of the earth. Again, as in the case of the earth, we could have breakfast at 8:00 A.M., lunch at 1:00 P.M., and dinner at 7:00 P.M. As long as the Martian day was set at 24 hours, this procedure would work out fine. Now there is nothing to prevent our dividing the Martian day up into any intervals we wished, and when we divide the day into 24 hours, it follows the familiar pattern to which we are subject on earth.

Divide the Martian day into 24 hours and the Martian hours must necessarily be longer than those used on earth. If a clock is built, it must possess more than one dial to give simultaneously the time for both earth and Mars. The only problem would be a mechanical one in which the gearing for the two clocks would be in the ratio of the Martian day to the earth day. This, fortunately, is not too difficult a problem, but other complications present themselves.

Not only does the length of the day differ but the length of the month and the year are not the same. As we found out, because Mars is farther from the sun, it takes longer to swing around it, and therefore the year is longer—a year being defined as the time it takes a planet to completely circle the sun. The year is a fundamental period and also one of the most important timekeeping units.

Since Mars is about one and a half times as far from the sun as the earth, the year is almost twice as long. While the earth swings around the sun once in 365.242199 mean solar days (don't mind the big numbers; we are going to use all of them shortly), it takes Mars 686.979702 mean earth solar days. This corresponds to 669.599051 Martian sidereal days, or 668.599051 Martian solar days.

One interesting facet of the difference in the length of years is the age problem. Let's suppose you are 35 years old on the earth. On Mars you would only be about 19! And if you are 70 on earth, your Mars age would be almost 39. But before you begin to think the fountain of youth resides on Mars, it is well to contemplate that while the calendar indicates you are only 39, your body will insist you are 70. Incidentally the same thing is true of weight. If you are very much overweight, going to Mars will cut down your weight by over 60 per cent. But this won't do you a bit of good. You will still look precisely the same—so if you want to trim down, you will have to do it the hard way by actually dieting.

Now that the Martian year has been determined in rather precise units, let's build a Martian calendar.

A calendar must have a beginning, and arbitrarily this writer chose the date of the beginning of the Julian day epoch as the date of the beginning of the Martian calendar. This Julian day calendar should not be confused with the Julian calendar formulated by Julius Caesar in 45 B.C. The Julian day epoch was originated in honor of Julius Scaliger and was established in 1582. It simply expressed the date as the number of days which have elapsed since the beginning of the arbitrary "Julian era"—January 1, 4713 B.C. Thus that date also represents the year 0 and the beginning of the Martian calendar.

To begin the Martian calendar, an arbitrary date was chosen— the instant of midnight of December 31, 1953, the beginning of January 1, 1954; this was when the clock was designed. This corresponded to Julian day 2,434,743.5. The 0.5 must be used since the Julian calendar counts the day as from noon to noon while we count it from midnight to midnight. Now we are ready to construct our calendar.

Since: $\dfrac{2,434,743.5}{668.599051} =$ 3641.5 plus, it means that January 1, 1954, falls in the Martian year 3641.

We adopt 668.6 for the number of Martian solar days in the Mars calendar year. The 0.6 days can be accounted for by permitting two years out of every five to contain 668 days, and the other three years will then contain 669 days. However, this calendar is too long! And it is too long by $0.6 - 0.599051$, or 0.000949 Martian solar days per year. This means that the calendar will be out one day in about 1000 years. Therefore to keep the calendar in step we will drop one day every tenth century. Even with this adjustment there will still be a slight error. If from 0.001 (which corresponds to an error of one day in 1000 years) we subtract 0.000949, there results 0.000051 days. This means that the calendar will be wrong by this amount, but this amounts to only one day in 20,000 years. By comparison our Gregorian calendar, the one we use today, is out about one day in 3000 years.

There of course arises the question: Why do we have to have such a precise calendar for Mars? The reason lies in the fact that like the earth Mars has seasons. As we have read, the axis of Mars is tipped about 25 degrees to its path around the sun, and thus the sun will appear to climb up and down in the Martian sky during the Martian year. We have also discovered the Martian seasons are about twice as long as ours.

A calendar to be of any value must be synchronized with the seasons. To produce on Mars what corresponds to the earth's tropical year, it is necessary to include 0.6 day at the end of the year. This interval corresponds to the quarter days of our years which add up at the end of every four to give us an extra day in leap year. To take care of this 0.6 day the first and fourth year will contain 668 days while the second, third, and fifth will contain 669 days. In the longer year the extra day will be given to December.

The month used on the earth is the period of time during which the moon passes through its phases. The very word "month" is derived from "moonth," as it was called at one time. Because the moon passes through its phases in 29½ days, that is the length of the terrestrial month. This is a most convenient period of time for activities, as it is an intermediate unit of time between the week and the year. In fact, centuries ago the month was an important interval, and events were depicted as occurring many moons ago.

Once we reach Mars, this almost natural unit of time loses its significance. We can of course try to use the moons of Mars. When we use the inner moon, the month is almost a half day in length; and when we use Deimos, the month becomes about five and a half days. However, these periods of time are too short to be considered of sufficient length for timekeeping purposes. Therefore the month on Mars will not be tied to a natural phenomenon.

This writer has given considerable thought to a calendar for the 668-plus days for Mars. It is possible to build a 12-month calendar for the planet. Let's divide up the Martian year into quarters of 167 days apiece. Then if the first and second months of each quarter are given 56 days and the remaining third month of the quarter is given 55 days, the four quarters can be given the necessary number of days to complete the year. In Martian leap years December will be given 56 days. Thus the 668-day year for Mars can be broken up into equal quarters and equal halves. And there will be a uniformity and regularity to the Martian calendar which we on earth will possess only when we adopt the World Calendar.

The week is an arbitrary unit of time on the earth. It was originally put into the calendar by the Babylonians, who saw seven objects in the sky which moved against the star background. These were the sun, the moon, and the five naked-eye planets. That is why we have a seven-day week. How fortunate we are that the ancient Babylonians did not possess telescopes. If they had and had discovered all the planets today, we might be using a ten-day week—which, by some, might be considered a little long, especially those who already consider the seven-day week too long.

We can have a seven-day week on Mars, too. This works out rather conveniently, for the months of 56 days will be divisible by seven exactly eight times. This works very well in the first and second months of the quarters. However, the third month has 55 days, and here we run into trouble. Because the years are not divisible by seven, the Martian year, like the terrestrial one, will begin on a different day of the week every year.

A clock to demonstrate the earth-Mars time difference has been built by the Hamilton Watch Company under the guidance of the author. From the photograph it can be seen to possess a 15-inch face on which are found one primary and three secondary dials.

The big dials graduated for a 24-hour day denotes the time on Mars. The secondary dial at 6 o'clock tells the earth time for the Greenwich meridian. The dial at 3 o'clock is really an earth-calendar dial indicating the month on the top slit, the year on the bottom slit, and the rotating hand moving against a dial and indicating the day of the month. This dial is calibrated to 31 days.

The dial at nine o'clock indicates the Mars date. The month is seen in the top slit, the year in the bottom slit, and again there is the rotating hand which gives the day of the month. This dial is graduated to 56 days. Automatic devices in the rear of the dial face automatically turn the month when the proper number of days have elapsed. When December has been run through, not only does the month change but the year counter turns over to add another year.

The names of the Martian months have arbitrarily been given the same names as those on the earth. The only difference will be a small "m" to indicate the Martian month so that January in the Martian calendar will be designated Jan_m.

Life's Beginning

In the dawn of time when the earth was still warm and naked, when the rocks lay bare, when the waters had concentrated in what was to become the oceans, and countless deltas, lagoons, and mud flats bordered the seas, when the air seethed with a chemical turbulence, when the volcanoes were erupting and laced the sky with nascent subsurface particles, and when the sun shone with a fierce radiance which defies description—*then* life came to the earth.

It came in microscopic particles and was abysmally primitive. There were no cells, no organisms; countless eons were to elapse before the simplest protein molecules put in an appearance. What was present in the sea and the air were the most primitive of organic compounds, the first actors in the cosmic drama.

In that long-ago time dust particles of infinite variety and composed of innumerable elements and compounds were being shot from volcanoes with extraordinary violence to be hurtled skyward into the ozoneless atmosphere. On ascension they collided, intermingled, and brushed with molecules of methane, ammonia, hydrogen sulphide, and microscopic droplets of water. These seething chemical compounds clung tenaciously to the surface of the particles as they ascended, and the higher they rose the more intense was the ultraviolet radiation of the primitive sun.

Chemical reactions were constantly taking place. In the air the known gases were undergoing dramatic transformations. The ammonia, the methane, and the hydrogen sulphide were stimulated by the sun, and new compounds were synthesized. These were organic compounds as differentiated from the inorganic materials which surround us. The simplest of the amino acids, glycine, was probably the first product of the intense activity at that time.

After conception in the atmosphere of the earth the amino acids were susceptible to the continued short-wave radiations of the sun. Some immediately on forming were just as immediately destroyed by this penetrating radiation. Still others, perhaps a tiny fraction of the whole, were carried into heavy, protective, dense clouds which

153

made them rain down on the earth. A clearing in the sky would destroy some as the powerful radiation lanced through to disintegrate them. Again others would land on the waters and be swept out to the friendly, nourishing, sheltering, protective oceans.

Millions of years passed, and the oceans assumed a consistency of a thin soup. Perhaps as much as 10 per cent of the oceans consisted of the primitive organic compounds—the amino acids. Thus came into being the mass formation of the simplest organic compounds. Again for millions of years the organic compounds floated lazily in the seas, relentlessly reacting in increasing variety to produce further and more complex substances. These in turn possessed incredibly vast chemical potentialities which could lead to more and more complex molecular structures as transformations took place at varying speeds.

In addition to these various oxidation products of hydrocarbons, the alcohols, aldehydes, ketones, acids, etc., also came into being through various agencies. The hydrocarbons intrinsically possessed tremendous chemical potentialities. When they were washed into the sea, there were continued reactions among themselves and the elements in the sea to give rise to fantastic numbers of all sorts of complex molecular compounds. In synthesizing compounds the chemist makes use of strong acids, bases, temperatures, pressures, and even radiations to speed up the processes. In that long-ago time, through volcanic activity most of these were present as catalyzers to speed and promote organic compound reactions, one with another and in a multitude of directions. In that long-ago time Nature with her primitive violence may have provided the various metals, hydrogen, salts, and halogens as catalysts to spark the reactions which took place, just as later in the cosmic day she was to provide enzymes to spark and speed reactions in the living cell.

Let us represent the chemical structure of glycine as used by chemists. The keystone of this entire molecule is the ubiquitous carbon atom.

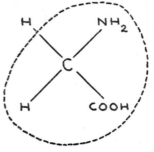

Notice that there are four ties coming off the carbon atom (center) in the above figure.

Here we find the fundamental foundation on which life like ours is based. Carbon plays a special role in the evolution of living organisms. Its chief claim to fame is that it is a tetravalent atom, which means that it can combine with four other elements to form complex molecules. It is obviously impossible to build up complex molecules with elements that are monovalent. As monovalent atoms they can combine only with a single other element, and the chain is closed. Bivalent elements are slightly better, trivalent ones still better, but tetravalent atoms seem to possess the maximum ability to unite with others. Of these carbon appears to possess more combining ability than any other element, and because of this unique property the tremendous diversity of organic substances has materialized.

The immediate result of this combining feature is the ability to form molecular chains and rings of extraordinary variety—for when it assumes the unique and peculiar chemical relationship with hydrogen, the building-up process is apparently limitless. The combination of carbon and hydrogen is the key to the production of the fantastically complex molecules which are the basis of life. It should be apparent that when carbon has combined with four other atoms, it is said to be saturated. However, and this is of utmost significance, if there should be free valences—that is, places in the molecule where ties to other atoms can be made—the carbon atoms may combine with each other. These compounds, however, are unsaturated and will readily combine with other atoms.

The combining, fissioning, developing, and splitting of organic compounds, curiously, can be reduced to three distinct types.

Oparin recognized three fundamental processes whereby organic matter could be transformed. The first reaction type was *condensation*, the combining of the simple compounds to produce long chains of organic matter, and the reverse process, which might be called *fission*, in which the organic chain was split between two adjacent carbon atoms. *Polymerization* was the second reaction in which there appeared a joining between two organic molecules through an atom of oxygen or nitrogen, and the reverse process, *hydrolysis*, which split the chains at the oxygen or nitrogen bond. The third process were the familiar *oxidation, reduction* reactions, which form the basis of the respiration process and of other oxidations occurring in the living cell and which intimately involves water.

Now let's return to our figure. It is immediately apparent that glycine is built up of the elements carbon, nitrogen, oxygen, and hydrogen, which we know existed in the primeval atmosphere. In this amino acid the part in the dotted circle is common to all the amino acids. The variation in the 25 amino acids simply comes from the change *in the one arm*.

Once more let's go back to the dawn of time. Let's begin with a molecule of CO_2. It is perfectly symmetrical and can be represented as $O = C = O$. Now imagine that this is subject to the sun's ultraviolet radiation or to lightning and this energy strips the oxygen atoms from the carbon dioxide leaving carbon, naked carbon. Similarly the short-wave radiations of the sun will break up water, molecular oxygen, and nitrogen. Thus the primordial molecules which can be represented in the figure below can be broken up as follows:

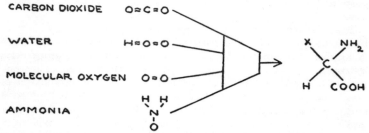

And under the same influence of radiation they can be combined to form the amino acid group in the right-hand part of the figure above, in which X represents a variety of molecules to form the various amino acids.

We know carbon has four valences which point in four directions evenly distributed; thus:

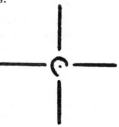

We can now begin at the top of the amino acid and build it up step by step in clockwise direction. And this time we will model another of the simplest amino acids, alanine.

For alanine we need three molecules in addition to carbon and hydrogen. We need molecules of the methyl group (CH_3), the amino

(NH_2), and the carboxyl group $(COOH)$. The manufacture of these groups is a well-understood, simple chemical reaction. It is the combining of these which presents some difficulty.

We start with the naked carbon atom and imagine it at "C," in the center of a three-sided pyramid, thus:

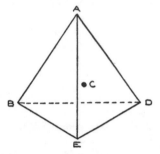

Now to the top of the pyramid we will add at "A" the methyl group so that we get:

Next comes the amino group, and as one place is as good as another, each will be adjoining the methyl, let's put it on the left corner at "B," thus:

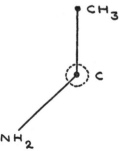

There are two places left, and again there is no way to distinguish one place from the other. Whether the carboxyl group goes to "E" or "D" corners, it will have the same environment: a methyl group, an amino group, and a free valence, all at the same distance from the carboxyl group and from each other. Thus in a chemical reaction which is governed purely by conditions of local affinity, it is apparent that among a large number of molecules just as many would react to put the carboxyl group at "E" as at "D." Therefore half should go to "E," the other half to "D," and the remaining valence will be filled by a hydrogen atom. But remember that our original compounds were all *symmetrical* in their anatomy. Now let's look at our amino acid models. Something new has appeared in that we have a structure which is *asymmetrical*. Although the relative arrangements of parts within the molecule is identical for these two types, their identity is not complete; they are as identical as your right and left hands; *i.e.*, as identical as two mirror images.

From this it is readily seen that in the building up of an amino acid from the raw materials of nature the probability of forming one mirror image is just as great as the probability of forming the other. Because both are equally probable, chemists have no way of arbitrarily synthesizing one mirror image or the other, by ordinary chemical means; *i.e.*, where the "chemistry of living matter" does not come into play. Only through the chemistry of living matter, and *only* through this agency, can a distinction be made between the two mirror images. In other words, in a game where the odds of getting head or tail are 50-50, Nature accomplished the highly improbable and gets 100 per cent heads—that is, all the amino acids of normal living protoplasm belong to the one mirror-image type exclusively. This type we call the l-type or the levorotatory type, because it has the property of rotating the plane of polarized light to the left, while the other mirror image—chemically identical—is the d-type—that is, it is dextrorotatory. This unique achievement of getting 100 per cent heads justifies the often quoted statement that life is a highly improbable state of matter.

The next step from the amino acids to the protein molecule is indeed a long one, and today there is nothing in man's physical experience which can be extrapolated to describe the transition. This step, as well as the next from protein molecule to cell, lies in the realm of sheer speculation.

Let us look at the amino-acid unit again. It possesses both acidic and basic components. The carboxyl group, COOH, is the acid one, while the amine group, NH_2, is the basic component. Let's liken the amino acid to a person. Each one has a left hand and a right hand. For amino acids to combine means that the acid component of one must combine with the basic component of the other.

Now let us imagine two long columns of people standing face to face, stretching out from a bandstand. Further, imagine that all the hands in the direction of the bandstand are acidic; those in the opposite direction, basic. If the group were to hold each other's hands so that they properly mated as in a hand clasp, the acidic hands on one side would clasp the basic hands on the other until the entire column was tied together through the medium of hands.

The same thing is true in the amino acids. The acidic component joins the basic component of the next amino acid, and this in turn can do the same thing. The net result of this type of combination is to create a long chain of amino acids tied together through nitrogen bands called the polypeptides. This is the whole basis of protein structure. The 25 amino acids combine in almost endless combinations of chains, and even these have links which tie the sides of the chains together. As a result an infinity of different patterns can occur, which gives rise to the extraordinary variety of proteins. There may be other arrangements of the atoms in the chain build-up, but the one which is best established and most obvious is the polypeptide structure. Residual valences also play a significant role in the building-up process. Separate amino-acid chains are united into large colloidal complexes by such residual valences.

Another significant fact is that the amino acids do not come together in loose masses like a pile of firewood. Rather they are fabricated into superbly organized structures like a crystal, albeit an unstable crystal.

Now what was the step from the large, complex protein molecules to the tiniest unit of life, the cell? Here is, biologists claim, a more difficult problem than that of the formation of the protein molecules. Amino acids can be synthesized, and the chemist can tie these into inordinately long chains. Thus it is possible to visualize the creation of the protein molecule except for its peculiar optical alignment— its asymmetry. But what do we do when we attempt to describe the protein-cell step?

Oparin points out that proteins, and other high molecular organic substances resembling them, form colloidal solutions in water. He shows that there are two types of colloids—the *hydrophil,* which have an affinity for water, and the *hydrophobe,* which remain dispersed in the water and cannot coagulate. The hydrophil colloids not only coagulate but can separate into two layers, one rich in colloidal material and a liquid layer or solution free of colloids. This phenomenon has been designated by de Jong as *coazervation*. The coazervate represents a special type of concentrated colloidal sol in which a separation is estblished between the shell of oriented water molecules and the free molecules of the equilibrium liquid. Oparin looks on coazervation as the most important event in the evolution of primary organic substances. While prior to this time the organic material was completely dissolved with its medium, with the formation of coazervates there occurred singular concentrations of the organic substances differentiated from the solution by a distinct, though not too sharp, boundary. Even with this zone of demarcation it was still possible for the coazervate to acquire from solution chemical substances to promote reactions. Here was a process whereby material from the environment was absorbed and converted into the colloidal body. This resulted in a growth of the primary coazervate, and to a certain degree the stage was being set for order and structure. Now to initiate life, properties of a supreme order had to be added to the coazervates which for better understanding we will call "collogels"—that is, colloidal gels. These were to make the colloidal system subject to biological laws.

Let's picture the earth when the colloids have evolved to a well-organized entity and the next stage of development was beginning. Two hundred millions years may have elapsed from the synthesis of the organic compounds to the appearance of these colloids. The earth was not static. Violent physical evolution had also put in an appearance penetrating every nook and cranny of the earth.

To begin, the earth had cooled, and no longer were the hot rocks in evidence. The warm seas still seethed with a multitude of highly complex molecular aggregations. Along the outlines of the seas the earth was studded with inlets where a certain stagnation of waters was present to give the collogels time to drink deeply of the concentrated chemical soup. Along the seas were high bluffs, the result of giant mountain-building processes. Volcanoes remained active, and the occasional peace and quiet of the primitive earth was shattered time after time by tremendous volcanic eruptions. As the earth cooled, the folding intensified, and overbearing stresses were set up in the rocks of the surface. When the rocks reached their elastic limit and ruptured, rearrangements took place in the form of earth-shattering quakes. Huge streams of water sped into the crack to the still-hot subsurface. Tremendous pressures were accumulated. Suddenly these proved too much for the overlying rocks, and new, vicious, violent volcanoes burst the stillness of the earth.

In the volcanic eruptions tremendous stores of "earth stuff" were blasted skyward. Gas, rock, steam, particles, and even virgin metals composed the stream that traveled skyward. The hot gases rising under this impact produced vertical turbulence, its fingers stretching high into the primitive atmosphere. The atmosphere was heavy. It reeked of hot acrid gases and water. Thunderstorms raged for interminable periods. Lightning lashed the earth with its forked tongue. The humidity was high; the air could hold no more water. Occasionally there came a clearing when the sun reached through to touch the earth, to create gusty hurricanic winds to churn and boil the water with its viciousness. Then a storm would close the gap again to present, once more, an unbroken atmospheric hydrosphere.

Concurrently tremendous activity took place in the seas.

When the moon reached its proper position in the sky giant tides would sweep mountains of water inland against the giant cliffs that ringed the oceans. Tremendous sprays, containing droplets of an infinite variety of sizes, would be set into motion, first reaching low levels and then cascading higher and higher as the turbulence imparted lift and speed to the droplets. Time after time, place after place, as the moon circled the earth and the earth circled the sun, the tide-raising forces sprang into play. The warm, thin soup of the ocean became airborne in an atmosphere of perfect "wetness" to preclude the spray's drying out.

This may have been the setting for the next act in the cosmic drama: the birth of the cell.

In the collogels the particles were assuming a definite position or orientation. A semblance of structure was putting in an appearance. In addition to pseudostructure each collogel was also acquiring an individuality because of the presence of the fantastic variety of molecular aggregates from which they sprang. Each collogel found itself with a singular physico-chemical structure. Heterogeneity was the order of the cosmic morning. Here was a powerful but subtle factor entering into the growth and development of these entities. They could absorb from the surrounding medium organic materials which too were governed by the particular physico-chemical characteristics.

There developed still greater increased variety from the absorbed substances. Foreign chemicals came into the collogel, some with disastrous results. In some instances there was degradation and perhaps disintegration. In other cases the addition of the native, raw, absorbed materials sparked the collogel to greater growth and with this increased order and structure. Patterns may now have entered the scene. Even at this early stage a selective process came into play, weeding the weak from the strong, giving rise to the persistence of highly developed and intrinsically stable collogels.

Something was still needed to breathe the spark of life into these collogels, and perhaps the environment furnished the mechanism for this step. To the writer it appears that *what was needed most to transform the dominant collogels into viable organisms was energy; primitive, powerful, short-wave, incisive energy.* Where was this energy to be had?

High above the murky atmosphere that clung tenaciously to the surface of the earth such energy existed. It was present in the penetrating photons of short-wave solar radiation. It was present in the highly ionizing, powerful primary cosmic rays that bombarded and are still bombarding the earth. The energy was available; how to bring it to the collogels? The answer may be that the energy did not come to the collogels; the collogels came to the energy.

Along the seacoast, where the battering wave sent swift spray into the sky, there may have been active volcanoes creating their vertical turbulence. Through the boundary of this upward-moving air the collogels may have penetrated. If so, they were carried through the murky atmosphere in company with incalculable numbers and types of chemicals from the volcanoes. These were present to act as catalysts, bringing together a growing organization and a promoter to increase the activity, the growth, the potentialities by incredible factors. And when this system reached high into the atmosphere, the necessary energy to change it from a dynamic collogel to a viable organism was available.

As the collogels were exposed to the powerful radiative influence, further chemical changes began taking place in the centers. It has been very well established that the combination of carbon dioxide, water, radiation, and the extreme variety of catalysts can give rise to formaldehyde—a plastic. In that long-ago time powerful bursts of radiation penetrated the collogel to transform some of its substance to a permeable plastic sheath of extreme thinness. In the center of this sheath was a "something" which, eons of terrestrial time later, was to evolve as the nucleus of the cell with its chromosomes, its nucleoli, and its centromeres. Here may have begun the first critical differentiation in the cell with the appearance of the nucleus set apart from the rest of the formative cell.

The plastic sheath was permeable—which meant that the primeval nucleus could still be nourished; it could still grow. It could still develop until finally size became a handicap. There would come a time when unless the nucleus could fission—break into smaller pieces—it lay in danger of degrading, losing order and structure, because the scale of chemical activity could not be accelerated to be operative in the next order of magnitude. Something had to give, and that something was the size of the nucleus. It was imperative that it become smaller, and it did so by dividing, by fissioning. Thus fissioning was introduced into the world—*the reproduction of the simplest organism we know.*

In the fissioning process the daughter cell would have been endowed with nucleus material and a protective shell of the plastic sheathing; and as the daughter separated, some of the remaining components of the collogel, what was to become the cytoplasm, would separate from the parent body to accompany her. And in this fluid there was also to evolve eons later the nitochondria, the golgi bodies, and the smaller plastids, the constituents of the cytoplasm as we know it today.

Now let us visualize the history of a daughter cell. It had been born in the upper reaches of the atmosphere where every conceivable chemical compound was present. From its atmospheric environment it obtained nourishment and was, like her mother before her, growing under ideal conditions. Whereas her ancestors had been collogels without a well-differentiated nucleus, the daughter started life with a well-differentiated nucleus. She may have returned to the seas to live, to thrive, to develop. More and more complex organic materials were offered to her, which she either accepted or rejected. There may have been considerable change in the surroundings of the nucleus, for the primitive cell had not yet acquired a sheath; only the nucleus was so protected. And in the many eons that elapsed, changes may have been taking place in the nucleus. The sheath was being transformed into a type of filter and so may have developed some immunity to the action of the primitive ultraviolet radiation.

After countless and identical descendants had come upon the earth, thinning the warm, soupy ocean of its life-giving compounds, once more the crashing tides sent these primitive cells high into the sky in the region of high-energy radiations. Now the same dynamic progressions which produced the plastic sheath surrounding the nucleus came into play to produce another sheath around the primitive cell prisoning the internal family forever. Once more the cells descended into the warm, fertile oceans, but this time as concrete entities. No longer was capricious nature to play fast and loose with the internal structure. No longer would primitive forces disrupt cells to lose their contents in the sea. The cell, the first living organism, had been given the breath of life. In the cosmic day it was high noon. Life had finally come to the earth.

How long ago did this process take place? Here once more we are dealing in the realm of sheer speculation. If we believe the universe was created six billion years ago, then 5.8 billion years ago the earth came into being. Millions of years elapsed until the hydrosphere was formed and the inorganic gases were carried into the sky to be transformed into organic compounds. Again millions of years passed to give rise to the protein molecules, and more millions passed until the first primitive cells came upon the scene. As a wild guess, I should say that the primitive cells were washed into the sea to grow, to develop, to evolve, to reach a new level of organization four billion years ago.

For the next 1.5 billion years the primitive cells climbed the evolutionary ladder becoming more complex and assuming a higher and higher magnitude of order and structure. Finally 2.5 billion years ago the cell had advanced to the point where it was ready to leave fossils. There are carbon specks in rocks which are believed to be 2.5 billion years old, bearing silent testimony to the age of these early single cells.

But the evolutionary trend did not cease. Now nature tried incalculable experiments with that early cell. Change, incessant change, was the order of the cosmic afternoon, and in that change the other elements of the cell structure were tried, weighed, tested, formed, and reformed to achieve an efficiency and a stability which would insure perpetuation. Cellular evolution was also filled with blind alleys. There was progression. There was stagnation. There was recession. But for every backward step dynamic Nature provided a change leading to still higher orders. For almost two billion years the seesaw rocked, finally to produce at some early pre-Cambrian epoch the finest, most complex, most precise handiwork of Nature—the final articulate living cell.

From this point on progress up the evolutionary ladder proceeded faster and faster until it came to man, the ultimate miracle of evolution. And in that march, by the very nature of the universal presence of life which developed, Nature shut the door on the possibility that this process ever could take place again on this earth.

BIBLIOGRAPHY

BIBLIOGRAPHY

Antoniadi, E. M. *La Planete Mars*. Librairie Scientifique, Hermann et Cie, Paris, 1930.

Bastin, Harold. *Plants Without Flowers*. Philosophical Library, New York, 1955.

Bernal, J. D. *The Physical Basis of Life*. Routledge & Kegan Paul, Ltd., London, 1951.

Blum, Harold F. *Time's Arrow and Evolution*. Princeton University Press, Princeton, 1951.

Butler, J. A. V. *Man Is a Microcosm*. Macmillan, New York, 1951.

Harbaugh, M. J. and Goodrich, A. L. (editors). *Fundamentals of Biology*. Blakeston Company, New York, 1953.

Henderson, Lawrence J. *The Fitness of the Environment*. Macmillan, New York, 1913.

Hess, S. L. "Some Aspects of the Meteorology of Mars," *Journal of Meteorology*, VII, 1950.

———. "Some Meteorology of Mars," *Sky and Telescope*, IX (1950), 155.

Jones, Spencer, H. *Life on Other Worlds*. Macmillan, New York, 1940.

Kuiper, G. P. *The Atmospheres of the Earth and Planets*. University of Chicago Press, Chicago, 1952. Revised Edition.

———. *Publication, Astronomical Society of Pacific*. Vols. 67, 271, 398.

Lowell, Percival. *Mars*. Houghton, Mifflin Company, Boston & New York, New York, 1895.

———. *Mars and Its Canals*. Macmillan, New York, 1906.

———. *The Evolution of Worlds*. Macmillan, New York, 1909.

———. *Mars As the Abode of Life*. Macmillan, New York, 1908.

Oparin, A. I. *Origin of Life*. Second translation, Dover, New York, 1953.

Russell, H. N., Dugan, R. S., and Stewart, J. Q. *Astronomy*. Ginn and Company, New York, 1938.

Scharonow, W. W. *The Brightness Contrasts Observed on the Surface of Mars*. Poulkovo Obser. Circular, No. 32, 1941.

Sherrington, Sir Charles. *Life's Unfolding*. C. A. Watts & Co., Ltd., London, 1943.

167

Slater, A. E. *Some Comments on Strughold's Ideas on Martian Vegetation.* J.B.I.S. XIII (3), 335.

Strughold, Hubertus. *The Green and Red Planet.* University of New Mexico Press, 1953.

Urey, H. C. *The Planets.* Yale University Press, Yale, 1952.

de Vaucouleurs, Gerard. *The Planet Mars.* Faber and Faber, London, 1950.

———. *Physics of the Planet Mars.* Macmillan, New York, 1954.

GLOSSARY

GLOSSARY

Albedo: The reflectivity of a planet.

Amino acids: Vital constituents of protein molecules.

Aphelion: The point in an orbit where a planet is farthest from the sun.

Eccentricity: The deviation of an ellipse or flattened circle from a circle.

Enzymes: Large protein molecules that act as catalysts.

Magnitude: A measure of the planet's brightness. The scale is such that a first-magnitude object is 2.5 times as bright as a second-magnitude object; a second-magnitude object is 2.5 times as bright as a third-magnitude object. A sixth-magnitude object under ideal conditions is theoretically visible to the naked eye. Extremely bright objects have negative magnitudes.

Maria: Latin for "seas." Dark areas on the moon were thought to be water before the complete absence of water was proven. The early designations are still used.

Milky Way: The band of faint light in the night sky produced by the concentration of the light of the faint stars in the central plane of the galaxy or star system of which the sun is one of 100 billion members.

Nodes: The intersection points of the plane of the satellite's path with the plane of the orbit of the planet, in this case Mars.

Oblateness: The flattening of a planet at the poles, due to rotation.

Opposition: Position of Mars (or other object beyond earth) when directly south at midnight. Closest approach occurs at or near date of opposition.

Perihelion: The point in an orbit where a planet is closest to the sun.

Phases: The sequence of changing appearance of the moon —a new moon, first quarter, full moon, and last quarter. Mars exhibits phases to a small extent sometimes appearing like the moon between eleven and seventeen days "old."

Quadrature: The positions of the sun, Mars, and earth in which the angle at the earth between the sun and Mars is 90°.

Radiometer: Device for measuring the entire radiation from an object, both visible and invisible.

Sidereal day: The length of time it takes for a planet to spin once on its axis with respect to the stars. The true period of rotation.

Sidereal year: The length of time it takes a planet to circle the sun. The true period of revolution.

Space station: A manned artificial satellite, circling the earth, of sufficient size to permit the crew to be self-sufficient for extended periods. A velocity of about five miles a second is necessary to establish it. For this reason relatively low speeds are necessary to depart from the space station to other celestial objects.

Subsolar point: The point on a planet where the sun is directly overhead.

Synodic year: The length of time it takes a planet to move from the south point around the sky and then back to the south point. The period from one opposition to the next.

Terminator: The sunrise or sunset line.

INDEX

173